LAB MANUAL
TO ACCOMPANY
APPLIED
CALCULUS
BY
RODNEY GENTRY

REVISED EDITION

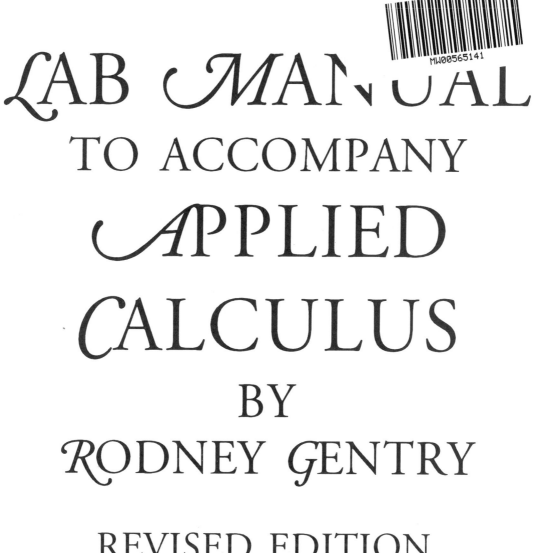

Joseph Cunsolo
Department of Mathematics and Statistics
University of Guelph

ADDISON-WESLEY

An Imprint of Addison Wesley Longman, Inc

Reading, Massachusetts • Menlo Park, California • New York • Harlow, England
Don Mills, Ontario • Sydney • Mexico City • Madrid • Amsterdam

Addison Wesley Custom Books consist of products that are produced from camera-ready copy. Peer review, class testing, and accuracy are primarily the responsibility of the author(s).

Manager of Addison Wesley Custom Books: Lynn Colgin
Production Administrator: Cindy Cody
Cover Design: John Callahan

ℒAB ℳANUAL TO ACCOMPANY 𝒜PPLIED 𝒞ALCULUS BY ℛODNEY 𝒢ENTRY
REVISED EDITION

ISBN: 0-201-33825-4

99 3

TABLE OF CONTENTS

Basic Review

Labs

Solutions to

Appendix

BASIC REVIEW

BASIC REVIEW

Welcome! This review material contains a brief summary of the essential mathematics you will need for this course. It is important that you do the associated review exercises to solidify this material as quickly as possible.

1. **BASIC SET THEORY NOTATION**

SUMMARY
You must know the meaning of the following symbols:

SYMBOL	MEANING
{ }	"the set of"
$\in$	"belongs to" or "is a member of"
$\notin$	"does <u>not</u> belong to" or "is not a member of"
$\cup$	"union"
$\cap$	"intersection"
$\emptyset$	"empty set"
$\subset$	"is a proper subset of"
$\subseteq$	"is a subset of"
$\not\subseteq$	"is <u>not</u> a subset of"

2. **THE REAL NUMBER SYSTEM SUMMARY**

$N = \{1, 2, 3,...\}$ "set of **NATURAL NUMBERS**"
$W = \{0, 1, 2, 3,...\}$ "set of **WHOLE NUMBERS**"
$I = \{...-2, -1, 0, 1, 2,...\}$ "set of **INTEGERS**"
$Q = \{\frac{p}{q} \mid p, q \in I, q \neq 0\}$ "set of **RATIONAL NUMBERS**"

PROPERTY OF RATIONAL NUMBERS

<u>Every</u> rational number $\frac{p}{q}$ can be expressed as either a

-**terminating decimal** (eg. $\frac{1}{4} = .25$, or $\frac{231}{100} = .231$)

-**repeating decimal** (eg. $\frac{1}{3} = .33\overline{3}$ or $\frac{3}{11} = .27\overline{2727}$).

IRRATIONAL NUMBERS

Irrational numbers are real numbers that have a non-repeating or non-terminating
decimal representation.

You can easily construct an example of an irrational number by creating a non-terminating and non-repeating pattern such as $0.01001000100001...$
where this pattern does not repeat because you are adding an extra 0 after each 1 and the decimal does not terminate because you can apply this process indefinitely.

Let **L** denote the set of irrational numbers.

KEY IRRATIONAL NUMBERS

SYMBOL   DECIMAL APPROXIMATION

$\sqrt{2}$ ≈ 1.41421356

π ≈ 3.14159265

e ≈ 2.71828183

(Note: get comfortable with these symbols. Remember that these symbols represent the actual irrational numbers, and the decimal representation is the <u>approximation</u> of the irrational number <u>not</u> the value of the irrational.)

SET OF REAL NUMBERS ℜ

The set of real numbers is the union of the set of rational numbers and the set of irrational numbers. $\Re = \mathbf{Q} \cup \mathbf{L}$

3. PROPERTIES OF EXPONENTS

NATURAL NUMBER EXPONENTS

Let x be a real number ($x \in \Re$) and m and n be natural numbers (m, n $\in$ **N**).

DEFINITION $x^n = x \cdot x \cdot x \ldots \cdot x \cdot x$ (n times)

EXPONENT PROPERTIES (x $\neq$ 0 and y $\neq$ 0)

1. $x^n \cdot x^m = x^{n+m}$

2. $(x^n)^m = x^{nm}$

3. $\dfrac{x^n}{x^m} = x^{n-m}$

4. $x^0 = 1$ (x $\neq$ 0)

5. $x^{-n} = \dfrac{1}{x^n}$ (also $\dfrac{1}{x^{-n}} = x^n$)

6. $(xy)^n = x^n y^n$

7. $\left(\dfrac{x}{y}\right)^n = \dfrac{x^n}{y^n}$

RATIONAL EXPONENTS PROPERTIES

If x^r, y^r, and x^s are defined, where r and s are reduced rational numbers, then the following are true.

1. $x^r \cdot x^s = x^{r+s}$

2. $(x^r)^s = x^{rs}$

3. $\dfrac{x^r}{x^s} = x^{r-s}$ x $\neq$ 0

4. $(xy)^r = x^r y^r$

5. $\left(\dfrac{x}{y}\right)^r = \dfrac{x^r}{y^r}$ y $\neq$ 0

4. \boxed{\text{ALGEBRA OF POLYNOMIALS}}

\boxed{\text{PRODUCTS AND FACTORING}}

\boxed{\text{SUMMARY of SPECIAL PRODUCTS}}

1. $(x + y)^2 = x^2 + 2xy + y^2$

2. $(x - y)^2 = x^2 - 2xy + y^2$

3. $(x + y)(x - y) = x^2 - y^2$

4. $(x + y)(x^2 - xy + y^2) = x^3 + y^3$

5. $(x - y)(x^2 + xy + y^2) = x^3 - y^3$

6. $(x + y)^3 = x^3 + 3x^2y + 3xy^2 + y^3$

7. $(x - y)^3 = x^3 - 3x^2y + 3xy^2 - y^3$

*Note that reading the Special Products formulas from **right to left** gives you the **basic factoring formulas.** so don't look at these charts as two separate charts to memorize since they are identical except for the order!!!*

\boxed{\text{SUMMARY OF FACTORING USING SPECIAL PRODUCTS}}

PERFECT SQUARE
$$x^2 + 2xy + y^2 = (x + y)^2$$
$$x^2 - 2xy + y^2 = (x - y)^2$$

DIFFERENCE OF SQUARES
$$x^2 - y^2 = (x + y)(x - y)$$

SUM OF CUBES
$$x^3 + y^3 = (x + y)(x^2 - xy + y^2)$$

DIFFERENCE OF CUBES
$$x^3 - y^3 = (x - y)(x^2 + xy + y^2)$$

PERFECT CUBES
$$x^3 + 3x^2y + 3xy^2 + y^3 = (x + y)^3$$
$$x^3 - 3x^2y + 3xy^2 - y^3 = (x - y)^3$$

5.   **INEQUALITIES**

The following summarizes the tools and properties needed to help solve inequalities

INEQUALITY SYMBOLS	
SYMBOL	VERBAL TRANSLATION
$>$	is greater than
$\geq$	is greater than or equal
$<$	is less than
$\leq$	is less than or equal

Properties of Inequalities

If $x, y \in \Re$, and $x > 0$, $y > 0$ then   (i) $x + y > 0$
                                                 (ii) $xy > 0$

If two numbers are positive then their sum and product is positive

If $x \in \Re$, then either   (i) $x > 0$ or   (ii) $x < 0$ or   (iii) $x = 0$

Any real number is either positive, negative, or zero.

Transitive Property (also true for $>$, $\geq$, $<$, and $\leq$)

If $x, y, z \in \Re$ such that $x < y$ and $y < z$ then $x < z$

For any three numbers, if the first is less then the second and the second is less then the third then the first number must be less than the third number.

Addition Property   (also true for $>$, $\geq$, $<$, and $\leq$)

If $x, y \in \Re$ and $x < y$ then for any $z \in \Re$, $x + z < y + z$

Adding the same number to both sides of an inequality does not change the direction of the inequality.

Multiplication Property   (also true for $>$, $\geq$, $<$, $and \geq$)
For $x, y , z \in \Re$ and $x < y$ then

$\quad$ (i) if $z > 0$,   then $xz < yz$
$\quad$ (ii) if $z < 0$,   then $xz > yz$

(i) Multiplying both sides of an inequality by a positive number does not change
$\quad$ the direction of the inequality.
(ii) Multiplying both sides of an inequality by a negative number reverses the
$\quad$ direction of the inequality.

Squaring Property   (Note that x and y are both positive.)

$\quad$ If $x, y \in \Re$, and $x > 0, y > 0$ then

$$x < y \text{ if and only if } x^2 < y^2$$

If two numbers, x and y, are postive and if x is less than y then the square of x is lless than the square of y. Note that this is not always true if the two numbers are not both positive. For example $-3 < 2$ but $(-3)^2 = 9 > 2^2 = 4$.

Reciprocal Property   (Note that x and y are both positive.)
$\quad$ If $x, y \in \Re$, and $x > 0, y > 0$ then

$$x < y \quad \text{if and only } \frac{1}{x} > \frac{1}{y}$$

For two postive numbers, x and y, if x is less than y then the reciprocal of x $(\frac{1}{x})$ is greater than the reciprocal of y $(\frac{1}{y})$ and vice versa. For example since $2 < 3$ then it follws that $\frac{1}{2} > \frac{1}{3}$ and the vice versa means that since $\frac{1}{5} > \frac{1}{8}$ then it follows that $5 < 8$.

6.   **INTERVAL NOTATION**

   Solution sets to inequalities are usually expressed in interval notation. In the following summary you will notice that intervals are just special sets of real numbers determined by inequalities.

Bounded Intervals

Interval Notation	Set Definition	Real Line Graph
(a, b)	$\{\, x \mid x \in \Re,\ a < x < b \,\}$	(#########) \ a \ \ b
[a, b]	$\{\, x \mid x \in \Re,\ a \leq x \leq b \,\}$	[#########] \ a \ \ b
(a, b]	$\{\, x \mid x \in \Re,\ a < x \leq b \,\}$	(#########] \ a \ \ b
[a, b)	$\{\, x \mid x \in \Re,\ a \leq x < b \,\}$	[#########) \ a \ \ b

Unbounded Intervals

Interval Notation	Set Definition	Real Line Graph
(a, +∞)	$\{\, x \mid x \in \Re,\ x > a \,\}$	(############# \ a
[a, +∞)	$\{\, x \mid x \in \Re,\ x \geq a \,\}$	[############# \ a
(−∞, a)	$\{\, x \mid x \in \Re,\ x < a \,\}$	#############) \ a
(−∞, a]	$\{\, x \mid x \in \Re,\ x \leq a \,\}$	#############] \ a
(−∞, +∞)	Set of all real numbers	#############

7.   **THE ABSOLUTE VALUE AND ABSOLUTE VALUE INEQUALITIES**

Absolute Value

The absolute value of a real number x, denoted by $|x|$, is a real number ≥ 0 and defined by

$$|x| = \begin{cases} x & if\ x \geq 0 \\ -x & if\ x < 0 \end{cases}.$$

Examples: $|5| = 5$, $|0| = 0$, $|-3| = 3$, $|-2.5| = 2.5$

Properties Of The Absolute Value

The following properties will help in working with absolute values

(i) $|x| \geq 0$ for all $x \in \Re$
The absolute value of any number is allways greater than or equal zero.

(ii) $|-x| = |x|$
A number and its negative have the same absolute value, e.g.
$|-5| = |5| = 5$

(iii) $|x - y| = |y - x|$
The absolute value of the difference of two numbers does not change if you reverse the order of the difference, e.g.
$|5 - 9| = |9 - 5| = |-4| = |4| = 4.$

(iv) $|x|^2 = x^2$
The square of the absolute value of number equals the square of the number.

(v) $\left|\dfrac{x}{y}\right| = \dfrac{|x|}{|y|}$ $y \neq 0$
The absolute value of a quotient is equal to the quotient of the absolute values. eg. $\left|\dfrac{3}{-7}\right| = \dfrac{|3|}{|-7|} = \dfrac{3}{7}$

(vi) $|x \cdot y| = |x| \cdot |y|$
The absolute value of a product is the product of the absolute values.

(vii) $\sqrt{x^2} = |x|$
The square root of a square of number is equal to the absolute value of the number, e.g. $\sqrt{(-3)^2} = \sqrt{9} = 3 = |-3|.$

Absolute Value Inequalities

Listed below is a summary of the basic absolute value inequalities and their solutions. Notice that the absolute value inequality is transformed into an equivalent inequality form which contains no absolute values.

Notation Reminder: $\Leftrightarrow$ means if and only if

Inequality	$\lvert x \rvert < a \Leftrightarrow -a < x < a$	$\lvert x \rvert \leq a \Leftrightarrow -a \leq x \leq a$
Sol'n Set	$(-a, a)$	$[-a, a]$

Graph	——(//////////)——
	     -a a
		——[//////////]——
		     -a a

Inequality	$\lvert x \rvert > a \Leftrightarrow x > a$ OR $x < -a$	$\lvert x \rvert \geq a \Leftrightarrow x \geq a$ OR $x \leq -a$
Sol'n Set	$(-\infty, -a) \cup (a, +\infty)$	$(-\infty, -a] \cup [a, +\infty)$

Graph	//////////)——(//////////
	     -a a
		//////////]——[//////////
		     -a a

SOLVING ABSOLUTE VALUE INEQUALITIES

Listed below are the basic types of absolute value inequalities you may encounter. Included is the FIRST LINE OF THE SOLUTION which removes the absolute value from the inequality and makes it easier to solve. These "first lines of the solution" in the first four inequalities were obtained by applying the above four absolute value inequalities.

Type	*First Line Of The Solution*
Assume that a and b are constants and a > 0 for the first four types	
$\lvert x - b \rvert < a$	$\Leftrightarrow \quad -a < x - b < a$
$\lvert x - b \rvert \leq a$	$\Leftrightarrow \quad -a \leq x - b \leq a$
$\lvert x - b \rvert > a$	$\Leftrightarrow x - b > a$ OR $x - b < -a$
$\lvert x - b \rvert \geq a$	$\Leftrightarrow x - b \geq a$ OR $x - b \leq -a$
$\lvert x - a \rvert < \lvert x - b \rvert$	$\Leftrightarrow \quad (x - a)^2 < (x - b)^2$
$\lvert x - a \rvert \leq \lvert x - b \rvert$	$\Leftrightarrow \quad (x - a)^2 \leq (x - b)^2$

REVIEW

Exercise I *(Algebra)*

1. Factor the following completely.
   (a) $x^3 + x^2y + xy^2$ (b) $x^2 - 25$ (c) $x^2 + 10x + 25$
   (d) $x^2 - 6x + 9$ (e) $x^3 - 1$ (f) $x^2 + 7x + 12$ (g) $x^2 - 3x - 18$
   (h) $x^3 + 6x^2 + 12x + 8$

2. Simplify.
   (a) $\dfrac{x^4 - 27x}{x^3 + x^2 - 12x}$ (b) $\dfrac{(x+h)^2 - x^2}{h}$, $h \neq 0$

   (c) $\dfrac{\sqrt{x+h} - \sqrt{x}}{h}$, $h \neq 0$ (d) $\dfrac{\frac{1}{x+h} - \frac{1}{x}}{h}$, $h \neq 0$

3. Solve for x.
   (a) $x^2 - x - 42 = 0$ (b) $x^2 - 5x + 4 = 0$ (c) $x^2 + 4x + 2 = 0$

   (d) $2x^2 + 5x + 1 = 0$

Exercise II *(Intervals and Functions)*

1. Express the following sets using interval notations. (Note that x is a real number.)

   (a) $\{\, x \mid -1 \leq x \leq 5 \,\}$ (b) $\{\, x \mid -23 < x \leq 3.5 \,\}$
   (c) $\{\, x \mid |x| < 3 \,\}$ (d) $\{\, x \mid x > -3 \,\}$
   (e) $\{\, x \mid x < 20 \,\}$ (f) $\{\, x \mid x < -2 \text{ or } x \geq 3 \,\}$
   (g) $\{\, x \mid x^2 \geq 5 \,\}$ (h) $\{\, x \mid |x - 2| < 5 \,\}$

2. Sketch the graphs and determine the domains and ranges of the following functions.

   (a) $f(x) = \begin{cases} -1 & \text{if } x < 0 \\ 1 & \text{if } x \geq 0 \end{cases}$ (b) $g(x) = \begin{cases} 3 & \text{if } x \leq -2 \\ 1 & \text{if } -2 < x \leq 1 \\ -1 & \text{if } x > 1 \end{cases}$

(c) **The Absolute Value Function** $y = |x|$ where $|x|$ is the absolute value of x,

$$\text{i.e. } |x| = \begin{cases} -x & \text{if } x < 0 \\ x & \text{if } x \geq 0 \end{cases}.$$

(d) **The Greatest Integer Function** $y = [x]$ where $[x]$ denotes the greatest integer less than or equal to x,

     i.e. $[x] = n$, n integer and $n \leq x < n+1$.

Examples $[3] = 3$, $[-2] = -2$, $[5.2] = 5$, $[-3.3] = -4$.

(e) $f(x) = \dfrac{|x|}{x}$ (f) $f = \{(1, 2), (2, 1), (3, -1)\}$

(g) $h = \{(-1, 2), (0, 2), (1, 2), (2, 2)\}$

Exercise III   (*Algebra of Functions*)

1.   Evaluate f(2), f(0), f(-1), f(x+h), f(x+1), f(2x), and f(f(x)) for the following:
     (a) $f(x) = x+1$ (b) $f(x) = x^2 + 1$ (c) $f(x) = \sqrt{x}$ (d) $f(x) = x^3 + 1$

2.   Find the natural domains of the following functions. (*Recall that the Natural Domain of a real function f is the largest subset D of all real numbers such that f(x) is defined for each element x of D.*)

   (a) $f(x) = 3x + 2$ (b) $f(x) = \sqrt{x}$ (c) $g(x) = \sqrt{x - 7}$

   (d) $h(x) = \dfrac{x}{x^2 - 1}$ (e) $P(x) = \dfrac{\sqrt{x}}{x^2 - 1}$ (f) $H(x) = \dfrac{\sqrt{x - 3}}{\sqrt{x + 3}}$

3.   Find the natural domain of the following pairs of functions f and g and evaluate $f+g$, $f-g$, fg, $\dfrac{f}{g}$, $\dfrac{g}{f}$, $-f$, $\dfrac{1}{f}$ and their respective domains.

   (a) $f(x) = x + 3$, $g(x) = x^2 + 2$ (b) $f(x) = 2x + 1$, $g(x) = \sqrt{x + 1}$

   (c) $f(x) = x$, $g(x) = x^2 - 1$ (d) $f = \{(2, 4), (3, 9), (4, 6), (5, 7)\}$
                 $g = \{(2, 2), (3, 3), (4, 2), (5, 1)\}$

   (e) $f = \{(1, 3), (2, 2), (3, -1), (4, 0)\}$
     $g = \{(1, 0), (3, 4), (4, -1)\}$

Exercise IV *(Polynomials)*

1.   Determine the equation of each of the following lines and sketch the graph:
(a) the line with slope 2 and y-intercept -3
(b) the line with slope -2 and passing through $(2, -5)$
(c) the line passing through $(-3, 4)$ and $(5, -2)$.

2.   Rewrite the following linear equations in the **slope-intercept** form and state the slope and y-intercept.
(a) $3x - 5y + 6 = 0$ (b) $-2x + 7y - 1 = 0$
(c) $y + x = 0$ (d) $2y + 3x = 2$

3.   (a) Sketch the graph of $f(x) = x^2$ and state its domain and range.

(b) Sketch the graphs of the following functions and state their domains and ranges. Compare the shapes and positions of these graphs with the graph of $y = x^2$.
(i) $y = -x^2$ (ii) $y = x^2 + 2$ (iii) $y = x^2 - 2$ (iv) $y = (x - 2)^2$
(v) $y = (x+2)^2$ (vi) $y = 2x^2$ (vii) $y = \frac{1}{2}x^2$

(c) Using the observations in part (b), obtain the graphs of the following functions by making the appropriate **shifts** to the graph of $y = x^2$.
(i) $y = x^2 + 3$ (ii) $y = x^2 - 3$ (iii) $y = (x - 3)^2$
(iv) $y = (x + 3)^2$ (v) $y = -x^2 + 1$ (vi) $y = -x^2 - 2$
(vii) $y = (x - 1)^2 + 3$ (viii) $y = -2(x - 2)^2 - 1$

Hint: *in parts (v) $\rightarrow$ (viii) transform the graph of x^2 one step at a time, e.g., in (viii):* $x^2 \rightarrow (x - 2)^2 \rightarrow 2(x - 2)^2 \rightarrow -2(x - 2)^2 \rightarrow -2(x - 2)^2 - 1$

4.   The results of question 3 can be extended to any function $y = f(x)$. Using the observations obtained in question 3, complete the following: (assume the constant $c > 0$)

(i) The graph of $y = f(x) + c$ is the graph of $y = f(x)$ shifted_____ c units.

(ii) The graph of $y = f(x) - c$ is the graph of $y = f(x)$ shifted_____ c units.

(iii) The graph of $y = f(x - c)$ is the graph of $y = f(x)$ shifted_____ c units.

(iv) The graph of $y = f(x + c)$ is the graph of $y = f(x)$ shifted_____ c units.

(v) The graph of $y = -f(x)$ is the graph of $y = f(x)$ _____about the x-axis.

5.   Using the results of question 4 and the given graphs find the following graphs.

(a)

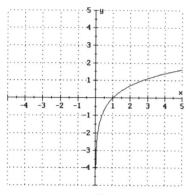

$$y = f(x)$$
$$(y = \ln(x))$$

$$y = f(x - 1)$$
$$(y = \ln(x - 1))$$

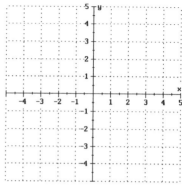

$$y = f(x + 2)$$
$$(y = \ln(x + 2))$$

(b)

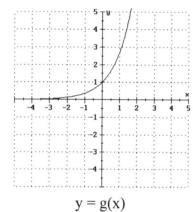

$$y = g(x)$$
$$(y = e^x)$$

$$y = g(x) + 2$$
$$(y = e^x + 2)$$

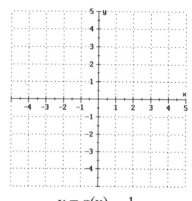

$$y = g(x) - 1$$
$$(y = e^x - 1)$$

(c)

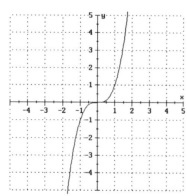

$$y = h(x)$$
$$(y = x^3)$$

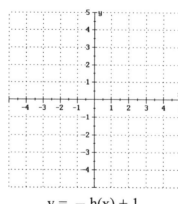

$$y = -h(x) + 1$$
$$(y = -x^3 + 1)$$

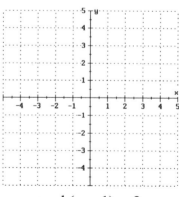

$$y = h(x - 1) - 2$$
$$(y = (x - 1)^3 - 2)$$

6.   Sketch the graphs of the following functions and from their graphs determine their ranges.

(a) $f(x) = \begin{cases} x^2 & \text{if } x \le 1 \\ x+1 & \text{if } x > 1 \end{cases}$

(b) $f(x) = \begin{cases} x & \text{if } x < -2 \\ x+2 & \text{if } -2 \le x < 0 \\ 2 & \text{if } x \ge 0 \end{cases}$

(c) $g(x) = \begin{cases} x-3 & \text{if } x < 4 \\ x+3 & \text{if } x \ge 4 \end{cases}$

(c) $g(x) = \begin{cases} -x^2 & \text{if } x \le 1 \\ x+1 & \text{if } x > 1 \end{cases}$

L A B S

LAB 1

PART A. Problems For Group Discussions

1. Linear Modelling Functions

Linear functions

Basic Form :	$y = mx + b$

$$\text{Slope}: \quad m = \frac{y_2 - y_1}{x_2 - x_1}$$

y-intercept : b *Graph* :   *Straight line*

Example with slope $m > 0$	*Example with slope* $m < 0$
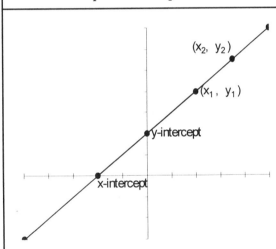	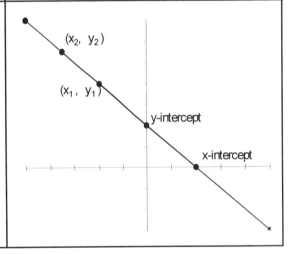

Determining a linear function or equation

Slope intercept form: $y = mx + b$
     Used when you are given the slope m and the y-intercept b.

Slope point form: $y - y_1 = m(x - x_1)$
     Used when you are given the slope m and a point on the line (x_1, y_1).

Two point form: $y - y_1 = \left(\frac{y_2 - y_1}{x_2 - x_1}\right)(x - x_1)$
     Used when you are given two points on the line, (x_1, y_1) *and* (x_2, y_2).

Quadratic Modelling Functions

Quadratic Function

$$Basic\ Form: \qquad y = ax^2 + bx + c$$

$$Alternate\ form: \qquad y = A(x-B)^2 + C$$

$$Factored\ form: \quad y = A(x - x_1)(x - x_2)$$

$$Graph: \quad parabola$$

$If\ a > 0\ or\ A > 0$	$If\ a < 0\ or\ A < 0$
then parabola concave up	*then parabola concave down*
sample graph	*sample graph*
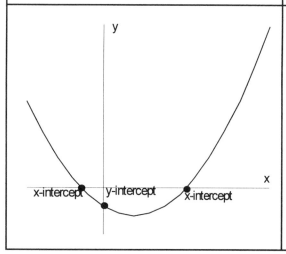	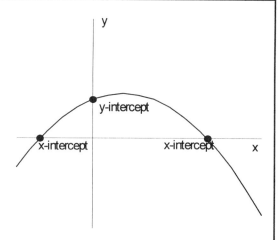

Quadratic Formula

Finds the roots of the equation. Geometrically you are finding the x-intercepts. Recall if it has 2 real distinct roots, then the graph crosses the x-axis twice at two different points. If it has 1 repeated root then it has the x-axis as its tangent and if it has no real roots (complex roots) then the graph does not cross the x-axis at all. For $ax^2 + bx + c = 0$

$$Quadratic\ Formula: \qquad x = \frac{-b \pm \sqrt{b^2 - 4ac}}{2a}$$

1.   (a) Rewrite $f(x) = 2x^2 - 12x + 23$ in the **Shifted form** : $f(x) = C(x - B)^2 + A$

   (b) Use the **Factored form:** $f(x) = k(x - x_0)(x - x_1)$ to find the equation of the quadratic function satisfying $f(-3) = 0$, $f(5) = 0$, and $f(7) = 5$.

2.   Absolute Value Function
   Sketch the graph and state the domain and range.

3.   Greatest Integer Function
   Sketch the graph and state the domain and range.

PART B   Supplementary Problems

Sketch the graph and state the domain and range of each of the following functions.
Note that $[\![x]\!]$ denotes the greatest integer of x and $|x|$ denotes the absolute value of x.

1. $y = \dfrac{x}{|x|}$ 2. $y = \dfrac{|x|}{x}$

3. $y = x + |x|$ 4. $y = x - |x|$

5. $y = x|x|$ 6. $y = x + [\![x]\!]$

7. $y = x - [\![x]\!]$

LAB 2

PART A. Problems For Group Discussions

1. On joining a real estate firm, an employee must choose one of two salary options based on the monthly net profit. Let x denote the monthly net profit in dollars.

    Option A   The monthly salary A(x) is $1,000 plus 4% of the monthly net profits.

    Option B   The monthly salary B(x) is $1,300 plus 5% of the monthly net profits greater than $15,000.

    (a) Express the monthly salaries A(x) and B(x) explicitly as functions of the monthly net profit x.

    (b) For what interval of monthly net profits is the monthly salary in Option B greater than in Option A?

    (c) Graph A(x) and B(x).

2. Quadratic Functions
    Recall that if a quadratic function is in the form $y = A(x - B)^2 + C$, then you can quickly determine the value of its maximum or minimum and where it occurs by remembering the following:
    (i)   if $A > 0$ ($\cup$) then y has a **MINIMUM VALUE** of C at $x = B$.
    (ii) if $A < 0$ ($\cap$) then y has a **MAXIMUM VALUE** of C at $x = B$.

    (a) Express the quadratic function $y = \frac{1}{3} (t^2 - 4t + 1)$ in the form
         $y = A(t - B)^2 + C$; state its maximum or minimum value, where it occurs, and sketch the graph.

    (b) Which of the following quadratic functions has its minimum value of 30 at x = 3?
         (A) $y = 3(x - 3)^2 - 30$ (B) $y = 5(x + 3)^2 + 30$
         (C) $y = 4(x - 3)^2 + 30$ (D) $y = - 3(x - 3)^2 + 30$
         (E) $y = 3(x - 30)^2 + 3$

    (c) In an epidemic, assume that the number of people infected is a quadratic function of the number of days the epidemic has been running with no people being infected a day t = 0. If the epidemic lasts 60 days and infects 450 people at its peak, then find the following:
         (i) the quadratic function model,
         (ii) the number of people infected on the 20th day.

PART B   Supplementary Problems

1. Sketch the graphs and state the domains and ranges of the following functions:

    (a) $y = |x - 3| - 2$ (b) $f(x) = [\![x]\!] - x$

    (c) $f(x) = \begin{cases} x^2 & \text{if } x \le 0 \\ x - 1 & \text{if } x > 0 \end{cases}$

2. Express the following quadratic functions in the form of $y = c(x - b)^2 + a$; state the maximum or minimum value and where it occurs, and sketch the graph.

    (a) $y = -2x^2 + 12x - 15$ (b) $y = \frac{1}{4}(x^2 + 6x + 1)$

3. Which of the following quadratic functions has its maximum value of -20 at $x = 2$?

    (a) $y = 2(x - 2)^2 - 20$ (b) $y = -(x - 2)^2 + 20$

    (c) $y = -3(x - 2)^2 - 20$ (d) $y = -(x + 2)^2 - 20$

    (e) $y = -(x - 2)^2 + 20$

4. What would be the percents of the monthly net profits in Option A and Option B of question 1 (PART A) that would make the monthly salary of Option B greater than that of Option A for monthly net profits of $x < \$6,000$ and $x > \$37,500$ and less than or equal Option A for $\$6,000 \le x \le \$37,500$?

5. In an epidemic, assume that the number of people infected is a quadratic function of the number of days the epidemic has been running. If the epidemic lasts 40 days and infects 800 people at its peak, then find the following:
    (i) the quadratic function model,
    (ii) the number of people infected on the 30th day.

LAB 3

PART A. Problems For Group Discussions

1. In a certain culture the rate of growth of bacteria is proportional to the amount present, If there are 2,000 bacteria present initially and 3,000 bacteria present 8 minutes later, then how much time is required to obtain 500,000 bacteria?

2. The temperature of a body discovered at midnight was 27.5 °C and the ambient temperature was a constant 21 °C . The body was quickly taken to the morgue where the ambient temperature was maintained at 4.4 °C. After one hour the body temperature was found to be 13.5 °C. Estimate the time of death.

3. Carbon Dating

    All living matter contains the radioactive isotope ^{14}C and its level remains constant as the decayed ^{14}C is constantly being replaced by ^{14}C absorbed from the carbon in the atmosphere. Cosmic radiation forms new ^{14}C in the atmosphere and keeps the level of ^{14}C in the atmosphere constant. The levels of ^{14}C in living matter and in the atmosphere are essentially the same. At death, the replacement of ^{14}C in the organism ceases and the level begins to drop slowly because of the radioactive decay of the ^{14}C.

    If we compare the amount of ^{14}C left in a particular sample to the amount of ^{14}C that occurs naturally in the atmosphere (and hence to the amount that was in the sample at the time of death), we can calculate the age of the sample. Note that the half-life of ^{14}C is 5685 years.

    (a) Find the decay factor for ^{14}C.

    (b) If a human bone is 500 years old then what percentage of the original ^{14}C is left in the bone?

PART B   Supplementary Problems

1. Find the function whose graph is the graph of $f(x) = log(x - 1) + 2$ shifted 3 units to the left and then 3 units downward.

2. If $2\ log_3(2) + log_3(x+1) = log_3(x+8)$ then find x.

3. Find $f^{-1}(x)$ given that $f(x) = 3e^{2x} - 5$.

4. Sketch the graphs of the following functions and state their domains and ranges.

   (a) $y = log(|x|)$ (b) $y = log_2(\llbracket x \rrbracket)$ for $1 \le x < 3$ (c) $y = \llbracket log_4(x) \rrbracket$ for $\frac{1}{4} \le x < 4$.

5. In a certain culture the rate of growth of bacteria is proportional to the amount present. If there are 1,000 bacteria present initially and the amount doubles in 12 minutes, then how much time is required to obtain 1,000,000 bacteria?

6. The half life of radium is approximately 1,600 years. Starting with 150 mg of pure radium find the amount left after t years. After how many years will only 30 mg remain?

7. Assume that the weights of a radioactive substance on the 2rd and 5th days of an experiment were 30 grams and 20 grams respectively.

   (a) What is the decay rate of the substance?

   (b) What is the half-life $t_{\frac{1}{2}}$ of this substance?

   (c) How much of the substance was present at the beginning of the experiment?

8. An organic specimen is found to contain 25% of the original ^{14}C. How old is the specimen if the half-life of ^{14}C is 5685 years.?

LAB 4

PART A. Problems For Group Discussions

1. A biological variable y varies sinusoidally with period 30 days, attaining its maximum at t = 12 days. If the maximum and minimum values are 44 and 24 respectively, obtain a formula for y as a sine function. Sketch the graph.

2. Which of the following equations has a graph that passes through $(1, 400)$ and when plotted on semi-log graph paper yields a straight line.

   (a) $y = 200x + 200$ (b) $y = 400x^2$ (c) $y = 200(4^x)$

   (d) $y = 200(2^x)$ (e) $y = 400 \, log(10x)$

3. The surface area, SA, of a person of a fixed weight is an allometric function of the person's height H. An experiment consisted of measuring the height and surface area of persons of the same weight (approximately). The values, two of which were $(10, 531)$ and $(100, 2{,}818)$, were plotted on log-log graph paper and a line was fitted to then data.
   (Note: Use $log(531) \approx 2.725$ and $log(2.818) \approx 3.450$)

   (i) State the general form of the equation for SA as a function of H.

   (ii) Determine the constants c and k in the above equation.

PART B   Supplementary Problems

1. A biological variable $y(t) = a \cos(k\pi t - b) + c$ where k, a, b, and c are constant varies sinusoidally with period 40 days, attaining its minimum at $t = 15$ days. If the maximum and minimum values are 65 and 25 respectively, obtain a formula for y and state the values of the constants k, a, b, and c.

2. Which of the following has basic period 3?

   (a) $y = \cos(\frac{3}{2} x)$ (b) $y = \sin(\frac{2}{3} \pi x)$ (c) $y = \cos(\frac{1}{3} x)$

   (d) $y = \sin(\frac{2}{3} x)$ (e) $y = \cos(3\pi x)$

3. Which of the following equations has a graph that passes through (2, 400) and when plotted on semi-log graph paper yields a straight line.

   (a) $y = 100(2^x)$ (b) $y = 400 \, log(5x)$ (c) $y = 100(4^x)$

   (d) $y = 100x + 200$ (e) $y = 400x^2$

4. Data from an experiment, including (4, 3) and (16, 6), was plotted on log-log graph paper. A straight line was fitted to the data. Determine the function $y = f(x)$ whose graph when plotted on log-log paper is this straight line.
   (Note: Use $log(4) \approx 0.6$, $log(3) \approx 0.47$, $log(16) \approx 1.2$ and $log(6) \approx 0.77$)

LAB 5

This is the week of your first term test examination. For your personal review and self-test, a sample termtest has been included below. After studying the material, write this termtest under examination conditions. The allotted time for this termtest is 1 hour. At the end of the hour, stop writing and mark your paper using the solutions with the indicated marking scheme which are found in the back of this manual. Good luck!

PART I
Each question in this part has exactly one correct answer. Circle your choice.

1. If $f = \{(1, 3), (3, -1), (5, 0), (7, 2)\}$ and $g = \{(0, 3), (1, 4), (3, -2), (7, 0)\}$ then which of the following is FALSE?

   (A) $g - f = \{(1, 1), (3, -1), (7, -2)\}$

   (B) $g \circ f = \{(1, -2), (5, 3)\}$

   (C) $-f = \{(1, -3), (3, 1), (5, 0), (7, -2)\}$

   (D) $\frac{1}{g} = \{(1, \frac{1}{4}), (3, -\frac{1}{2})\}$

   (E) $\frac{g}{f} = \{(1, \frac{4}{3}), (3, 2), (7, 0)\}$

2. Let $f(x) = x^5 - 1$ and $g(x) = x^3$ then which of the following is FALSE?

   (A) $(g - f)(x) = x^3 - x^5 + 1$

   (B) Domain of $(\frac{g}{f}) = (-\infty, 1) \cup (1, +\infty)$

   (C) $(f \circ g)(x) = x^8 - 1$

   (D) $(g \circ f)(x) = (x^5 - 1)^3$

   (E) $(fg)(x) = x^8 - x^3$

3. The natural domain of $\dfrac{ln(x+3)}{4-x^2}$ is

(A) $(-3, +\infty)$

(B) $[-3, -2) \cup (-2, 2) \cup (2, +\infty)$

(C) $(2, +\infty)$

(D) $(-3, -2) \cup (-2, 2) \cup (2, +\infty)$

(E) $(-3, 2) \cup (2, +\infty)$

4. Let $f(x) = \begin{cases} 3^x & \text{if } x \leq 1 \\ |x+3| & \text{if } x > 1 \end{cases}$.

Which of the following is the range of f?   (Hint: a sketch may be helpful.)

(A) $[0, 3) \cup [4, +\infty)$
(B) $(0, +\infty)$
(C) $(0, 3) \cup (4, +\infty)$
(D) $(-\infty, +\infty)$
(E) $(0, 3] \cup (4, +\infty)$

5. If $3e^{4x-7} = 8$ then x equals

(A) $\frac{1}{4} ln\left(\frac{8}{3}\right) + \frac{1}{4} ln(7)$

(B) $\frac{1}{4}\left(ln\left(\frac{8}{3}\right) + 7\right)$

(C) $\frac{1}{4} ln\left(\frac{8}{3}\right) + 7$

(D) $4\left(ln\left(\frac{8}{3}\right) + 7\right)$

(E) $\frac{1}{4}\left(ln(8) - 7\right)$

6. Suppose in a certain lake, the bass population size, B, is given by
$B(n) = 40 + \sqrt{\dfrac{n}{120}}$ where n is the minnow population size. The minnow
population size is given by $n(p) = 2p + 3$ where p is the amount of plankton in
the lake. The bass population size B as a function of the plankton p is given by

(A) $83 + 2\sqrt{\dfrac{p}{120}}$

(B) $40 + 2\sqrt{\dfrac{p + 3}{120}}$

(C) $80\,p + 120 + \sqrt{\dfrac{p}{120}}$

(D) $40 + \sqrt{\dfrac{2p + 3}{120}}$

(E) $40 + 2\sqrt{\dfrac{p}{120}}$

7. Let $f(x) = \dfrac{1}{3}(x - 5)^{\frac{1}{3}} + 4$. The inverse function f^{-1} is given by $f^{-1}(x)$ equals

(A) $(3x - 4)^3 + 5$

(B) $3(x - 4)^3 + 5$

(C) $27(x - 5)^3 + 8$

(D) $27x^3 + 1$

(E) $27(x - 4)^3 + 5$

8. If $2 \log_7(10x) - \log_7(25) = 2$ then x equals

   (A) $\dfrac{35}{2}$

   (B) $\dfrac{7}{2}$

   (C) $\pm \dfrac{35}{2}$

   (D) $\pm \dfrac{7}{2}$

   (E) $\dfrac{245}{4}$

9. The basic period of $y = 7\cos(5\pi x - 5) + 11$ is

   (A) $10\pi^2$

   (B) $\dfrac{2}{5}$

   (C) 10

   (D) $\dfrac{2}{5}\pi$

   (E) $\dfrac{5}{2}$

10. Which one of the following equations represents the sketched graph?

   (A) $f(x) = -\dfrac{1}{2}x + 4$

   (B) $f(x) = \dfrac{1}{16}(x - 8)^2$

   (C) $f(x) = (x - 8)^{\frac{2}{3}}$

   (D) $f(x) = (x - 8)^3$

   (E) $f(x) = 8 e^x - 4$

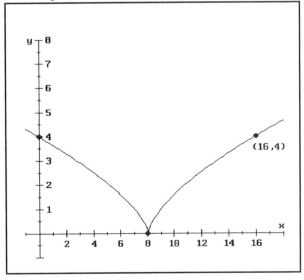

11. Which of the following has a graph that is the graph of $f(x) = \sin(x+2) - 2$ shifted to the right 4 units and then shifted upwards 3?

(A) $y = \sin(x - 4) + 3$

(B) $y = \sin(x - 2) + 1$

(C) $y = \sin(x - 2) - 5$

(D) $y = \sin(x + 6) + 1$

(E) $y = \sin(x + 6) - 5$

12. Which of the following equations passes through the point (8, 3200) and when plotted on semi-log graph paper yields a straight line?

(A) $y = 800(\frac{1}{2})^x$

(B) $y = 1600\,(2)^{\frac{x}{4}}$

(C) $y = 10x + 3120$

(D) $y = 800\,x^{\frac{2}{3}}$

(E) $y = 100\,(2)^{\frac{5x}{8}}$

PART II
Work each problem. Show all your work in the space provided.
13. Sketch the graphs of the following functions on the associated axis and for the indicated x's. Label at least two points on each graph.

2

(A) $y = 4 \sin(\frac{\pi}{2}x - \pi)$ for $-4 \leq x \leq 5$

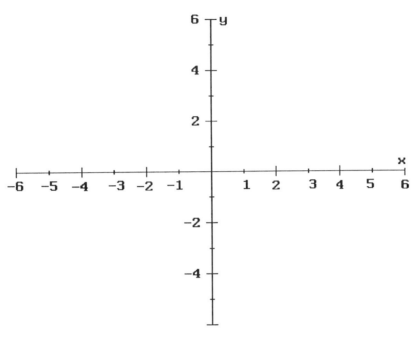

(B) $y = 2^{[x]}$ for $-1 \leq x < 3$ (where $[x]$ is the greatest integer of x)

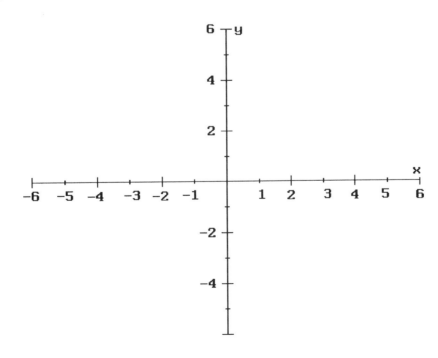

14. A pulsating light pulses so that the strength of the light emitted in one pulse is a quadratic function of time. Suppose that one pulse lasts 60 seconds and that the light strength at the beginning and end of each pulse is 0 candles. Express the light strength over one pulse as a function of time, given that the maximum strength in each pulse is 300 candles.

15. $\boxed{\textbf{Area} - \textbf{Species Curve}}$ It has been found that the number of species S of a given taxon on an island is an allometric function of the area A of that island, $S = c(A)^k$. If research data indicates that the graph of this function is a straight line on log − log graph paper passing through the points corresponding to $(A, S) = (1, 2.8)$ and $(A, S) = (100, 70.3)$ then determine the following:
NOTE: USE $\log (2.8) = 0.45$ and $\log (70.3) = 1.85$

$\boxed{2}$

(i) the constant c

(ii) the constant k

16. The fallout from a nuclear explosion contaminated a Pacific Ocean island with the radioactive component Strontium-90, which has a half − life of 28 years. Readings from the island indicated that the level of Strontium-90 was 20 times the level considered safe for human habitation.

2

  (i) State the model equation describing the Strontium-90 level as a function of time.

  (ii) What is the decay factor k of Strontium 90?

  (ii) How long after the contamination will the island become safe for human habitation?

LAB 6

PART A. Problems For Group Discussions

1. An animal is given 15 grams of a drug on the first day of an experiment. The dosage is increased by 3 grams each successive day.

    (a) List the dosages for the first 5 days of the experiment.

    (b) If the experiment ends when the dosage for one day reaches 120 grams, how many days did the experiment last?

    (c) If the experiment lasts 41 days, what is the total amount of the drug that will be required?

2. A certain bacteria culture is found to increase by 10% every generation, The initial size of the culture is 8,000 bacteria and at each generation, after the increase, 400 bacteria are removed and used in another experiment.

    (a) State the difference equation representing the change in size of the culture per generation.

    (b) Find the size of the bacteria culture at the nth generation.

3. A new park is designated to have a buffalo herd. Due to normal mortality, the herd size is expected to decrease by 10% each year. The initial size of the herd is 1,000 buffalo and each year, after the decrease, 50 additional buffalo are added.

    (a) State the difference equation representing the change in size of the herd per year.

    (b) Find the size of the herd at n years.

    (c) What will be the eventual size of the herd?

    (d) How many buffalo would have to be added to the herd each year if the desired eventual size of the herd is 2,500 buffalo?

PART B   **Supplementary Problems**

1.   An immunologist prescribes an immunization treatment in which the patient is given daily doses of a certain snake venom.   Suppose that the patient receives a 3 unit dose on the first day and that each day the dosage is increased by 2 units.
      (a) List the dosages for the first 5 days of the treatment.
      (b) Express as a series the total amount of venom that the patient will have received after the nth dose and sum the series.
      (c) If the treatment lasts for the 60 days what is the total amount of venom needed.

2.   A certain bacteria culture is found to decrease in size by 20% every generation. The initial size of the bacteria culture is 2,000 bacteria and each generation after the decrease, an additional 200 bacteria are added.

      (a) State the difference equation representing the change in size of the culture per generation.

      (b) Find the size of the bacteria culture at the nth generation.

      (c) What will be the eventual size of the bacteria culture?

3.   A new park is designated to have a buffalo herd. Due to normal mortality, the herd size is expected to decrease by 20% each year. The initial size of the herd is 1,000 buffalo and each year, after the decrease, 80 additional buffalo are added.

      (a) State the difference equation representing the change in size of the herd per year.

      (b) Find the size of the herd at n years.

      (c) What will be the eventual size of the herd?

      (d) How many buffalo would have to be added to the herd each year if the desired eventual size of the herd is 2,500 buffalo?

4.   Each year, a bank deducts $10 as service charges on each deposit account, and then pays 5% interest on the remaining money.   If X_n denotes the amount in specific account at the end of year n.

      (a) Write a difference equation satisfied by the sequence $\{X_n\}$.
      (b) Write an expression giving the balance of the account at the end of year n if the
          initial deposit X_o is $1,000.
      (c) What initial deposit will result in the account neither growing nor diminishing?

LAB 7

PART A. Problems For Group Discussions

1. Evaluate the following:

    (i) $\displaystyle\lim_{x \to 0} \frac{\sqrt{x+4}-2}{x}$

    (ii) $\displaystyle\lim_{x \to 5} \frac{\frac{1}{x+5}-\frac{1}{10}}{x-5}$

2. Let $f(x) = \begin{cases} x^3+7 & \text{if } x \le -2 \\ -1 & \text{if } -2 < x \le 1 \\ x^2-1 & \text{if } x > 1 \end{cases}$

    (a) Compute the following:

    (i) $\displaystyle\lim_{x \to -2^-} f(x)$ (ii) $\displaystyle\lim_{x \to -2^+} f(x)$ (iii) $\displaystyle\lim_{x \to -2} f(x)$

    (iv) $\displaystyle\lim_{x \to 1^-} f(x)$ (v) $\displaystyle\lim_{x \to 1^+} f(x)$ (vi) $\displaystyle\lim_{x \to 1} f(x)$

    (b) Is f continuous at x = − 2? Explain your answer.

    (c) Is f continuous at x = 1? Explain your answer.

3. A drug is administered every six hours in doses of 5 mg. The drug is neutralized at an exponential rate with decay rate constant k = 0.2. Not all the drug is neutralized before the next dose is administered. Denote by A(t) the amount of drug in the patient's system at time t (hours).

    (a) Compute $\displaystyle\lim_{x \to 6^-} A(t)$. Note that this is the drug left from the first dose.

    (b) Give the formula for the function A(t) and sketch the graph of A(t) over the successive intervals [0, 6), [6, 12), and [12, 18).

    (c) Determine the residual amount of the drug in the patient's system at the end of the nth dosage period.

PART B   **Supplementary Problems**

1.   Evaluate the following:

(i) $\lim_{x \to 0} \dfrac{\sqrt{x + 16} - 4}{x}$

(ii) $\lim_{x \to 4} \left(\dfrac{x^2 - 11x + 28}{x - 4} \right)$

(iii) $\lim_{x \to 0} \dfrac{\sqrt[3]{x + 1} - 1}{x}$

(iv) $\lim_{x \to -2} \dfrac{x^2 - x - 6}{x^2 + 3x + 2}$

2.   Let $f(x) = \begin{cases} [\![x]\!] & \text{if } x < 1 \\ 1 & \text{if } 1 \le x \le 2 \\ x^2 - 3 & \text{if } x > 2 \end{cases}$

(a)   Compute the following:

(i) $\lim\limits_{x \to 1^-} f(x)$ (ii) $\lim\limits_{x \to 1^+} f(x)$ (iii) $\lim\limits_{x \to 1} f(x)$

(iv) $\lim\limits_{x \to 2^-} f(x)$ (v) $\lim\limits_{x \to 2^+} f(x)$ (vi) $\lim\limits_{x \to 2} f(x)$

(b)   Is f continuous at $x = -1$? Explain your answer.

(c)   Is f continuous at $x = \frac{1}{2}$? Explain your answer.

(d)   Is f continuous at $x = 1$? Explain your answer.

(e)   Is f continuous at $x = 2$? Explain your answer.

LAB 8

PART A. Problems For Group Discussions

1. During the first ten years after planting, a tree was growing in such a way that the radius (in cm) of its trunk was given by $r(t) = 25 + 20t - t^2$ where t is time measured in years. Determine the average rate of change of its radius over this ten year period

2. Let $f(x) = \cos(\frac{\pi x}{2})$. Determine the equation of the secant line which passes through the initial point (2, f(2)) and which is determined by the increment $\triangle x = 1$.

3. Determine the equation of the tangent line to the graph of $f(x) = 6 \, ln(x)$ at (2, 6ln(2)).

4. A seething, undulating, extra-terrestrial blob grows in such a way that its volume in cubic metres in time t minutes is given by $V(t) = 30t - t^2$.

    (a) What is the rate of change of the blob's volume with respect to time when t = 4 minutes?

    (b) When will the blob's volume be increasing at a rate of 15 m³/min

    (c) When will the blob stop growing?

PART B   Supplementary Problems

1.   Suppose that the weight in milligrams of a population of bacteria changes according

      to the formula $P(t) = 50 + \dfrac{100t}{20 + t^2}$ where t is the time measured in hours.

      Determine the average rate of growth of the populations during the six hour period
      starting at t = 2 hours.

2.   Let $f(x) = 2 \sin(\frac{\pi x}{2})$.   Determine the equation of the secant line which passes
      through the initial point (2, f(2)) and which is determined by the increment $\triangle$ x=1.

LAB 9

This is the week of your second term test examination. For your personal review and self-test, a sample termtest has been included below. After studying the material, write this termtest under examination conditions. The allotted time for this termtest is 1 hour. At the end of the hour, stop writing and mark your paper using the solutions with the indicated marking scheme which are found in the back of this manual. Good luck!

PART I

Each question in this part has exactly one correct answer. Circle your choice.

1. Which of the following arithmetic sequences has constant difference $d = 6$ and the 42nd term $a_{42} = 248$.

    (A) $\{10, 14, 18,...\}$ ✗
    (B) $\{4, 10, 16,...\}$
    (C) $\{2, 8, 14,...\}$
    (D) $\{6, 10, 14,...\}$ ✗
    (E) $\{3, 9, 15,...\}$

2. Which of the following is FALSE?

    (A) $\displaystyle\sum_{i=0}^{60} i = 1830$

    (B) $\displaystyle\sum_{i=1}^{25} 5(\tfrac{1}{3})^i = \tfrac{15}{2}\left(1 - (\tfrac{1}{3})^{25}\right)$

    (C) $\displaystyle\sum_{i=1}^{10} i^3 = \frac{100(121)}{4}$

    (D) $\displaystyle\sum_{k=8}^{24} (3^{k+1} - 3^k) = 3^{25} - 3^8$

    (E) $\displaystyle\sum_{i=5}^{21} 2 = 34$

3. $\displaystyle\sum_{n=1}^{60} (10n - 4)$ equals

   (A) 17,400

   (B) 17,700

   (C) 18,000

   (D) 18,060

   (E) 18,300

4. If a solution to $\triangle X_n = aX_n + b$ is $X_n = 540 - 300(\frac{2}{3})^n$ then the constant a equals

   (A) $\frac{1}{3}$

   (B) $-\frac{1}{3}$

   (C) $-\frac{2}{3}$

   (D) $\frac{2}{3}$

   (E) 1

5. The positive equilibrium for the difference equation $X_{n+1} = -X_n(X_n - 4) + 10$ is

   (A) 1

   (B) 2

   (C) 4

   (D) 5

   (E) 10

6. If $X_{n+1} = aX_n + 500$ where $0 < a < 1$ and the steady state $\overline{X} = \lim_{n \to +\infty} X_n = 800$ then the constant a equals

(A) $\frac{1}{4}$

(B) $\frac{3}{8}$

(C) $\frac{1}{2}$

(D) $\frac{5}{8}$

(E) $\frac{7}{8}$

7. $\lim_{x \to 7} \dfrac{\sqrt{35 + 2x} - 7}{x - 7}$ equals

(A) $+\infty$

(B) $\frac{1}{14}$

(C) $\frac{1}{7}$

(D) $-\frac{1}{7}$

(E) $-\frac{1}{14}$

8. If $f(x) = \dfrac{1}{x-3}$ then the difference quotient $\dfrac{\triangle f(x)}{\triangle x} = \dfrac{f(x+h) - f(x)}{h}$, $h \neq 0$ equals

(A) $\dfrac{-1}{(x-3)(x+h-3)}$

(B) $\dfrac{1}{(x-3)(x+h-3)}$

(C) $\dfrac{-1}{(x-3)^2 + h}$

(D) $\dfrac{-1}{x^2 - 9 + h}$

(E) $\dfrac{-1}{(x+h-3)^2}$

9. Let B(t) denote the biomass (in mg) of a bacteria culture at time (in hours). If the average rate of change of the biomass B(t) from t=3 to t=10 hours is $\dfrac{5}{21}$ mg/hour and B(3) = 9 then B(10) equals

(A) $10\,\tfrac{2}{3}$ mg

(B) $9\,\tfrac{5}{7}$ mg

(C) $9\,\tfrac{2}{3}$ mg

(D) $8\,\tfrac{2}{3}$ mg

(E) $8\,\tfrac{5}{7}$ mg

10. The slope of the tangent line to the graph of $f(t) = 2\,t^{-\frac{4}{3}}$ at the point $(1, f(1))$ is

    (A) $-\frac{5}{8}$

    (B) $-\frac{5}{2}$

    (C) $-\frac{6}{5}$

    (D) $\frac{7}{5}$

    (E) $-\frac{8}{5}$

11. If $y = \sec(x)$ then y'' equals

    (A) $\sec^3(x)\tan(x)$

    (B) $\sec^3(x) + \sec^2(x)\tan(x)$

    (C) $\sec^3(x) + \sec(x)\tan^2(x)$

    (D) $\sec(x)\tan(x) + \sec^2(x)$

    (E) $2\sec^2(x)\tan^2(x)$

12. If $f(x) = c\,x^{\frac{3}{2}} - 2x + 7$ where c is a constant and if the second derivative

    $f''(25) = 9$ then c equals

    (A) $\frac{27}{20}$

    (B) $\frac{12}{5}$

    (C) $\frac{14}{15}$

    (D) 60

    (E) 12

PART II

Work each problem. Show all your work in the space provided.

13. Let $f(x) = \begin{cases} 5\sin(4x) + 6 & \text{if } x < 0 \\ 6e^{-\frac{x}{3}} & \text{if } 0 \leq x < 6 \\ 2\ln(x-5) & \text{if } x \geq 6 \end{cases}$

(A) Compute the following:

(i) $\lim\limits_{x \to 0^-} f(x) =$

(ii) $\lim\limits_{x \to 0^+} f(x) =$

(iii) $\lim\limits_{x \to 6^-} f(x) =$

(iv) $\lim\limits_{x \to 6^+} f(x) =$

(B) Is f continuous at x = 0? Explain your answer.

14. Suppose that the size in milligrams of a cell culture is given by $M(t) = t + \dfrac{25}{t^2}$ for $t > 0.1$, where t is measured in hours.

   (A) At what rate is the size of the cell culture changing at t = 5 hours?

   (B) At what time will the growth rate of the culture be zero?

15. In an insecticide testing experiment on a controlled population of insects it was observed that each month, before the spraying, 400 insects were removed and the remaining insect population decreased by 10% as a result of the spraying. After the decrease, 500 insects were added to the population. Let X_n denote the size of the population at month n.

   (A) State the difference equation representing the change in size of the population each month.

   (B) If the initial population was 5,000 then find the size of the insect population at the end of the nth month.

16. A certain difference equation modelled by $X_{n+1} = f(X_n)$ corresponds to the following graph:

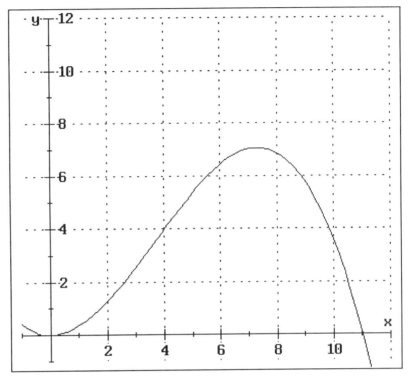

(A) Estimate the equilibriums of the system.

(B) If $X_5 = 3$ then estimate X_7.

(C) Is the largest equilibrium value stable or unstable? Illustrate on the diagram.

LAB 10

PART A. Problems For Group Discussions

1. For the function $f(x) = x^{\frac{4}{3}} - 4x^{\frac{1}{3}}$ determine

    (i) all the critical points,

    (ii) all local extrema,

    (iii) the intervals on which f is increasing and decreasing,

    (iv) the intervals over which the graph of f is concave upward and concave downward,

    (v) the point(s) of inflection.

    (vi) the x-intercepts (use factoring)

    Use this information to sketch the graph of $y = f(x)$.

2. In a peach orchard, it was found that the average number of peaches per tree was equal to $(800 - 8n)$ where n represents the number of trees per acre and n lies between 30 and 70. How many trees should be planted per acre to maximize the total yield of peaches per acre?

3. A cistern is to be constructed with a concrete square base, four concrete walls and a square steel top. If the cistern must hold 768 m³ of water and if the steel costs twice as much per unit area as the concrete, determine the dimensions of the cistern that will minimize the construction cost?

PART B   Supplementary Problems

1. Repeat question 1 in **PART A** using   (a) $f(x) = 3x^4 - 8x^3$,

   (b) $f(x) = x^{\frac{5}{3}} - 5x^{\frac{2}{3}}$.

2. A particular peach orchard has an average yield of 600 peaches per tree when it has 30 trees per acre. It was found that each additional tree planted per acre reduced this average yield by an average of 10 peaches per tree. How many trees should be planted per acre to maximize the total yield of peaches per acre?

3. At time t after injection, the concentration C(t) of a certain drug in the blood is given by

$$C(t) = \frac{A}{r - s} (e^{-st} - e^{-rt}),$$

   where A, r, and s are positive constants, with r > s. Find the value of t at which the concentration reaches a maximum.

LAB 11

PART A. Problems For Group Discussions

Definition:

If $\triangle y$ is the error in a quantity y then $\frac{\triangle y}{y}$ is the **relative error** in y and

$100(\frac{\triangle y}{y})$ is the **percentage error** in y.

Hence the **approximate relative error** in y is $\frac{dy}{y}$ and the **approximate percentage error** in y is $100(\frac{dy}{y})$

1. (a) Use differentials to determine the approximate increase in the surface area of a soap bubble when its radius increases from 2 cm to 2.0001 cm.

    (b) Find the approximate relative change in surface area of this bubble.

    (c) Find the approximate percentage change in the surface area of this bubble.

2. If the percentage error in computing the volume of a sphere is not to exceed 2%, then what is the approximate maximum percentage error that can be allowed in the measured value of the radius?

3. Find the equation of the tangent line to the graph of $2x^2 + x^2y^2 + y = 2x$ at the point $(1, -1)$.

4. Find the third degree (or order) Taylor polynomial approximation about $x = 1$ of the function $f(x) = xe^x$.

5. Approximate the value of $\cos(1.5\pi + .01)$ by using a 3rd order Taylor Polynomial approximation of the function $y = \cos(x)$ about $x_0 = 1.5\pi$.

PART B   **Supplementary Problems**

1. The gas in a spherical balloon contracts causing a reduction in the radius from 4 m to 3.95 m.

    (i)   What is the approximate change in the volume of the balloon?

    (ii)   What is the approximate change in the surface area of the balloon?

    (iii)   Find the approximate relative changes in the volume and the surface area of the balloon.

2. The radius of a sphere is found by measurement to be 3 cm but there is possible error of $\pm\,0.03$ cm in measurement. Find, approximately, the error and percentage error in the value of the surface area of the sphere that might occur because of the error in the radius.

3. The radius of the sphere is to be measured and its volume computed. If the radius can be accurately measured to within 0.1%, find (approximately) the maximum percentage error in the volume.

4. Find the equation of the tangent line to the graph of $x^2 + y^2 = e^{xy}$ at $(1, 0)$.

5. Find the third order Taylor Polynomial approximation about $x_0 = 1$ for $f(x) = ln(x)$.

6. Approximate the value of $\sin(1.5\pi + 0.01)$ by using a 4th order Taylor polynomial approximation of the function $f(x) = \sin(x)$ about $x_0 = 1.5\pi$.

7. Compute the approximate value of $\sqrt{4.24}$ using a third order Taylor polynomial approximation about $x_0 = 4$.

LAB 12

PART A. Problems For Group Discussions

1. Water escapes from a corroded pipe at the rate $R(t) = 3t^2 + 5$ litres/hour. Let $V(t)$ represent the amount of water (in litres) lost at time t hours.

    (i)   Represent $V(t)$ as an indefinite integral.

    (ii)   If the amount of water lost at the beginning of observation $(t = 0)$ was 5 litres, find the amount of water lost three hours later.

2. A patient is given a 16 mg dose of a drug at time $t = 0$. It is determined that the

    drug is being excreted at a rate of $3t^{\frac{1}{2}}$ mg/hr.

    (a)   Express as a function $D(t)$ the amount of the drug still in the patient a time t.

    (b)   When will the patient be drug free?

PART B   Supplementary Problems

1. Assume that the size of a bacteria culture increases at the rate

    $$r(t) = 3t^2 + t \quad \text{bacteria/hour}$$

    Let $P(t)$ represent the number of bacteria present at time t hours.

    (i)   Represent $P(t)$ as an indefinite integral.

    (i)   If $P(0) = 100$, find $P(2)$.

2. The number of revolutions per minute ($RPM(t)$) in an ultracentrifuge increases

    at a rate $f(t) = 3e^t$ over a period [0, T]. If $RPM(0) = 0$, find $RPM(T)$

    when $T = 5$.

COURSE REVIEW

For your personal review and self-test, a sample final exam has been included below. After studying the material, write this final exam under examination conditions. The allotted time for this final exam is 2 hours. At the end of the 2 hours, stop writing and mark your paper using the solutions with the indicated marking scheme which are found in the back of this manual. Good luck!

PART I

Each question in this part has exactly one correct answer. Remember to **CIRCLE** your answer on this questionnaire and clearly indicate your answer on the computer score sheet.

1. If $f(x) = e^{3x+4} - 2$, the inverse function f^{-1} is given by

 (a) $f^{-1}(x) = \dfrac{1}{e^{3x+4} - 2}$

 (b) $f^{-1}(x) = \frac{1}{3} ln(x + 2) + \frac{4}{3}$

 (c) $f^{-1}(x) = \frac{1}{3} ln(x + 2) - \frac{4}{3}$

 (d) $f^{-1}(x) = \frac{1}{3} ln(x + 4) - \frac{2}{3}$

 (e) $f^{-1}(x) = \frac{1}{3} ln(x + 4) + \frac{2}{3}$

2. If $\{a_n\}$ is an arithmetic sequence with $a_1 = 8$ and
 $a_{11} = 68$ then a_{31} is

 (a) 120

 (b) 168

 (c) 188

 (d) 198

 (e) 208

3. An equation that passes through (8, 200) and whose graph
    on log-log paper is a straight line with slope $\frac{2}{3}$ is

(a) $y = 200\, x^{\frac{2}{3}}$

(b) $y = 200\, (2)^{x-8}$

(c) $y = 200\, (2)^{\frac{2x}{3}}$

(d) $y = 50\, x^{\frac{2}{3}}$

(e) $y = \frac{2}{3}\, x + \frac{584}{3}$

4. Let $f(x) = \begin{cases} ln(2x^2 + 1) & \text{if } x \leq 0 \\ sin(\llbracket x \rrbracket) & \text{if } 0 < x < 1 \\ 3^{x-1} & \text{if } x \geq 1 \end{cases}$,

    where $\llbracket x \rrbracket$ is the greatest integer of x. Which of the following is false?

(a) $\lim\limits_{x \to \frac{\pi}{4}} f(x) = 0$

(b) $\lim\limits_{x \to 0^+} f(x) = 0$

(c) $\lim\limits_{x \to 0^-} f(x) = 0$

(d) $\lim\limits_{x \to 1^+} f(x) = 0$

(e) $\lim\limits_{x \to 1^-} f(x) = 0$

5. If $\triangle X_n = -\frac{1}{5} X_n + 300$ and $X_0 = 2500$ then X_n equals

    (a) $1300(-\frac{3}{5})^n + 700$

    (b) $1000(\frac{2}{5})^n + 1500$

    (c) $2000(\frac{4}{5})^n + 500$

    (d) $1750(\frac{4}{5})^n + 750$

    (e) $1000(\frac{4}{5})^n + 1500$

6. The equilibrium for the equation $\triangle X_n = -\frac{1}{3} X_n - 2$ is

    (a)   6

    (b)   3

    (c) $\frac{3}{2}$

    (d) $-\frac{3}{2}$

    (e) -6

7. A function with basic period 10 and a maximum value of 70 is

    (a) $30 \sin(\frac{\pi x}{5}) + 40$

    (b) $70 \sin(10x)$

    (c) $70 \sin(\frac{\pi x}{10})$

    (d) $70 \sin(\frac{\pi x}{5}) + 70$

    (e) $40 \sin(\frac{x}{5}) + 30$

8. If $2\left(\log_b(16) - \log_b(2)\right) + 3 = 9$ then b is

    (a) 2
    (b) e
    (c) 3
    (d) 4
    (e) 10

9. The population of a bacterial culture at time t, in hours, is given by $P(t) = 2^t$. The average rate of change of the population over the interval [3, 7] is

    (a) 28 bacteria/hr

    (b) 30 bacteria/hr

    (c) 32 bacteria/hr

    (d) 34 bacteria/hr

    (e) 36 bacteria/hr

10. If the size of the nth generation of a population of fruit flies is given by

    $P_n = 100 + \sum_{t=1}^{n} (t - 20)$, then which of the following is the size of the 200th generation?

    (a) 16000

    (b) 16100

    (c) 16200

    (d) 16300

    (e) 16400

11. Which of the following functions has a graph that is the same as the graph of $y = ln(2x)$, but shifted right 3 units and upwards 2 units?

   (a) $y = 2 + ln(2x+3)$

   (b) $y = 2 + ln(2(x+3))$

   (c) $y = 2 + ln(2(x - 3))$

   (d) $y = 2 + ln(2x - 3)$

   (e) $y = 3 + ln(2(x+2))$

12. Assume that the growth rate of a chicken, $R(t)$, is a quadratic function of the number of days t since the chicken was hatched. Assume that the chicken is not growing at hatching and ceases to grow after 80 days. If the chicken's maximum growth rate is $R_{max} = 10$, then the equation for $R(t)$ is:

   (a) $R(t) = -\dfrac{1}{160}(t - 40)^2 + 10$

   (b) $R(t) = \dfrac{1}{160}(t - 40)^2 + 10$

   (c) $R(t) = -\dfrac{1}{160}(t + 40)^2 + 10$

   (d) $R(t) = -\dfrac{1}{40}(t - 40)^2 + 10$

   (e) $R(t) = -\dfrac{1}{160}(t - 80)^2 + 10$

13. Which one of the following is **FALSE?**

   (a) The $(n + 1)$ th derivative of a polynomial of degree n is zero.

   (b) A function $f(x)$ is continuous at $x = a$ if $\lim_{x \to a} f(x) = f(a)$.

   (c) A function is increasing on (a, b) if x_1, x_2 in (a, b) and $x_1 < x_2$ implies that $f(x_1) > f(x_2)$.

   (d) The definite integral of a continuous function $f(x)$ over $[a, b]$ is given by $\int_a^b f(x)\, dx = F(b) - F(a)$ where $F(x)$ is an antiderivative of $f(x)$.

   (e) $\int_a^b k\, f(x)\, dx = k \int_a^b f(x)\, dx$ where k is a constant.

14. The population size $P(t)$ of a bacteria culture at time t (in hours) was given, by $P(t) = k(2+t)^3$ where k is a constant. If the rate of growth at $t = 2$ hours was 9600 bacteria/hour then the value of k is

   (a) 50
   (b) 100
   (c) 150
   (d) 200
   (e) 250

15. The distance s from a fixed point to a bead moving on a straight wire is related to the time t by $s(t) = t^2\sin(t)$. The acceleration $A(t)$ at time t is given by

   (a) $2\sin(t) + 4t\cos(t) + t^2\sin(t)$

   (b) $2\sin(t) - 4t\cos(t) - t^2\sin(t)$

   (c) $2t^2\sin(t) + 4t\cos(t)$

   (d) $2t\sin(t) + t^2\cos(t)$

   (e) $2\sin(t) + 4t\cos(t) - t^2\sin(t)$

16. $\displaystyle\lim_{x \to 9} \left(\frac{\frac{1}{x\text{-}6} - \frac{1}{3}}{x - 9} \right)$ equals

   (a) $+\infty$

   (b) $\frac{1}{9}$

   (c) 0

   (d) $-\frac{1}{9}$

   (e) $-\infty$

17. $D_x \left(e^{\cos^2(\sqrt{x})} \right)$

   (a) $\dfrac{2}{\sqrt{x}} \cos(\sqrt{x})\sin(\sqrt{x})\, e^{\cos^2(\sqrt{x})}$

   (b) $-\dfrac{2}{\sqrt{x}} \cos(\sqrt{x})\sin(\sqrt{x})\, e^{\cos^2(\sqrt{x})}$

   (c) $\dfrac{1}{\sqrt{x}} \cos(\sqrt{x})\sin(\sqrt{x})\, e^{\cos^2(\sqrt{x})}$

   (d) $-\dfrac{1}{\sqrt{x}} \cos(\sqrt{x})\sin(\sqrt{x})\, e^{\cos^2(\sqrt{x})}$

   (e) $\cos^2(\sqrt{x})\, e^{\cos^2(\sqrt{x})-1}$

18. If $x^2 + e^{xy} + y = 2x$ then y' equals

   (a) $\dfrac{2 - 2x}{xe^{xy} + 1}$

   (b) $\dfrac{2 - 2x - ye^{xy}}{xe^{xy}}$

   (c) $\dfrac{2 - 2x - xe^{xy}}{xe^{xy}}$

   (d) $\dfrac{2 - 2x - ye^{xy}}{xe^{xy} + 1}$

   (e) $\dfrac{2 - 2x - xe^{xy}}{ye^{xy}}$

19. $\int x \sqrt{5 - x^2}\ dx$ equals

    (a) $\frac{1}{3}(5 - x^2)^{\frac{3}{2}} + C$

    (b) $-\frac{1}{3}(5 - x^2)^{\frac{3}{2}} + C$

    (c) $\frac{2}{3}(5 - x^2)^{\frac{3}{2}} + C$

    (d) $-\frac{2}{3}(5 - x^2)^{\frac{3}{2}} + C$

    (e) $\frac{2}{3}x(5 - x^2)^{\frac{3}{2}} + C$

20. Which of the following is **false?**

    (a) The definite integral of f(x) over [a, b] is defined by

$$\int_a^b f(x)\ dx = \lim_{\substack{N \to +\infty \\ \triangle x \to 0}} \sum_{n=1}^{N} f(x_n^*) \triangle x_n.$$

    (b) An antiderivative of a function f(x) is a function F(x) such that $F'(x) = f(x)$.

    (c) The differential of $y = f(x)$ is defined by $dy = f'(x)dx$

    (d) The natural domain of the function $y = e^{-2x}$ is $(-\infty, +\infty)$.

    (e) The function $y = ln(x\text{-}2)$ is decreasing for all x in $(2, +\infty)$.

21. $\int_4^{16} \dfrac{dx}{\sqrt{x}}$ is equal to

    (a) 2

    (b) 4

    (c) 6

    (d) 8

    (e) 12

22. If $y = x^{(x^3)}$ then y' is equal to

(a) $x^2 + 3x^2\, ln(x)$

(b) $x^3 x^{x^3-1}$

(c) $x^{(x^3)}\left(x^2 + 3x^2\, ln(x)\right)$

(d) $3x^2\left(x^{x^3-1}\right)$

(e) $x^{(x^3)}\, x^3\, ln(x)$

23. $\int_0^\pi \cos(x)\sin^3(x)\, dx$ equals

(a) -1

(b) $-\frac{1}{4}$

(c) 0

(d) $\frac{1}{4}$

(e) 1

24. If 2,400 g of a radioactive material decays exponentially with decay rate $k = \frac{1}{200}$ then the number of grams of this material that is left by the time $t = 200\,ln(4)$ years is

(a) $\frac{2}{3}$

(b) 300

(c) 600

(d) 900

(e) 1,500

25. If the size of a cell culture at time t is given by the function $F(t) = te^{-\frac{1}{3}t}$ for t ≥ 0, then the size of the culture is a maximum when t equals

(a) 0

(b) $\frac{1}{3}$

(c) $\frac{1}{5}$

(d) 3

(e) 5

26. The third order Taylor polynomial approximation about $x_0 = 3$ of the

function $f(x) = e^{2x-6}$ is

(a) $1 + 2(x - 3) + 4(x - 3)^2 + 8(x - 3)^3$

(b) $1 + 2x + 4x^2 + 8x^3$

(c) $1 + 2x + \frac{2}{3}x^2 + \frac{4}{3}x^3$

(d) $1 + 2(x - 3) + 2(x - 3)^2 + \frac{4}{3}(x - 3)^3$

(e) $1 + 2(x+3) + 2(x+3)^2 + \frac{4}{3}(x+3)^3$

PART II

Work each problem. Show all your work in the space provided.

27. (a) Find the finite area bounded by the graphs of $f(x) = 3x$ and $g(x) = x^2 - x$.
        Sketch the area.
2

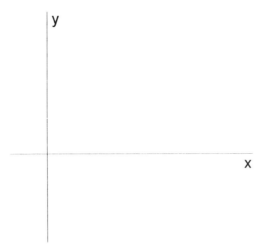

(b) A healing wound is circular in shape. The radius was $r = 3$ cm and 24
        hours later the radius was 2.8 cm. (The area of a circle is $A = \pi r^2$)
        (i) Use differentials to approximate the decrease in the area of the wound in
            the 24 hour period.

2

        (ii) Find the approximate relative percentage change in the surface area of
            the wound in the 24 hour period.

28. (a) A biological variable $y(t) = k \sin(a\pi t + b) + c$, where k, a, b and c are constants, varies sinusoidally with period 80 days, attaining its minimum at t = 40 days. If the maximum and minimum values are 95 and 35 respectively, determine the constants k, a, b and c.

2

(b) **Approximate** the definite integral $\int_{0}^{8} x e^{x}\, dx$ by using a uniform partition of size N = 4 and the right end point of each subinterval for evaluation (Do not attempt to evaluate the exponentials).

2

29. For the function $f(x) = 4x^3 - 12x^2 + 16$

    (a) Find all local extrema for $y = f(x)$.

Answer

    (b) Indicate the intervals on which the graph of $y = f(x)$ is concave upward and concave downward.

1

concave upward

concave downward

    (c) Find the points of inflection

1

Answer

(d) Sketch the graph of y = f(x). Label the local extrema points and points of
     inflection.

2

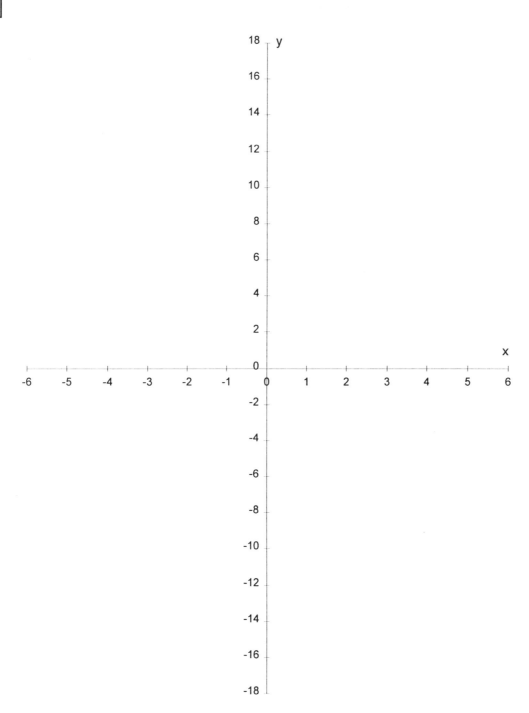

30. (a) A discrete dynamical system is given by the difference equation

$$X_{n+1} = f(X_n) \text{ where f is given by the graph}$$

3

(i) What are the equilibrums of this system?

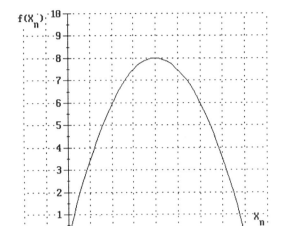

(ii) If $X_4 = 7$ estimate X_6.

(iii) Estimate the value X_0 for which the slope of the tangent line to the graph of f is one.

$X_0 =$

(b) Evaluate $\int_0^1 9x \sqrt{3x + 1} \, dx$.

2

SOLUTIONS

Solutions for Basic Review Exercises

Exercise I

1. (a) $x(x^2 + xy + y^2)$ (b) $(x+5)(x-5)$ (c) $(x+5)^2$

     (d) $(x-3)^2$ (e) $(x-1)(x^2+x+1)$ (f) $(x+3)(x+4)$

     (g) $(x-6)(x+3)$ (h) $(x+2)^3$

2. (a) $\dfrac{x^4 - 27x}{x^3 + x^2 - 12x} = \dfrac{x(x^3 - 27)}{x(x^2 + x - 12)} = \dfrac{(x-3)(x^2 + 3x + 9)}{(x-3)(x+4)} = \dfrac{x^2 + 3x + 9}{x + 4}$

     (b) $\dfrac{(x+h)^2 - x^2}{h} = \dfrac{x^2 + 2xh + h^2 - x^2}{h} = \dfrac{h(2x+h)}{h} = 2x + h \quad h \neq 0$

     (c) $\dfrac{\sqrt{x+h} - \sqrt{x}}{h} = \left(\dfrac{\sqrt{x+h} - \sqrt{x}}{h}\right)\left(\dfrac{\sqrt{x+h} + \sqrt{x}}{\sqrt{x+h} + \sqrt{x}}\right)$

$$= \dfrac{(\sqrt{x+h})^2 - (\sqrt{x})^2}{h(\sqrt{x+h} + \sqrt{x})} = \dfrac{x + h - x}{h(\sqrt{x+h} + \sqrt{x})} = \dfrac{h}{h(\sqrt{x+h} + \sqrt{x})}$$

$$= \dfrac{1}{\sqrt{x+h} + \sqrt{x}} \quad h \neq 0$$

     (d) $\dfrac{\left(\dfrac{1}{x+h} - \dfrac{1}{x}\right)}{h} = \dfrac{\left(\dfrac{x - (x+h)}{x(x+h)}\right)}{h} = \dfrac{x - x - h}{hx(x+h)} = \dfrac{-h}{hx(x+h)}$

$$= \dfrac{-1}{x(x+h)} \quad h \neq 0$$

3. (a) $(x-7)(x+6) = 0 \quad \Rightarrow \quad x = 7, \; x = -6$

     (b) $(x-4)(x-1) = 0 \quad \Rightarrow \quad x = 4, \; x = 1$

     (c) Use the quadratic formula: $x = \dfrac{-4 \pm \sqrt{4^2 - 4(1)(2)}}{2(1)} = \dfrac{-4 \pm \sqrt{16 - 8}}{2}$

$$= \dfrac{-4 \pm \sqrt{8}}{2} = \dfrac{-4 \pm 2\sqrt{2}}{2} = -2 \pm \sqrt{2}$$

(d) Use the quadratic formula: $x = \dfrac{-5 \pm \sqrt{5^2 - 4(2)(1)}}{2(2)} = \dfrac{-5 \pm \sqrt{25 - 8}}{4}$

$\qquad = \dfrac{-5 \pm \sqrt{17}}{4} \quad \text{or} \quad \dfrac{-5}{4} \pm \dfrac{\sqrt{17}}{4}$

Exercise II

1. (a) $[-1, 5]$ (b) $(-23, 3.5]$ (c) $(-3, 3)$

    (d) $(-3, +\infty)$ (e) $(-\infty, 20)$ (f) $(-\infty, -2) \cup [3, +\infty)$

    (g) $(-\infty, -\sqrt{5}] \cup [\sqrt{5}, +\infty)$ (h) $(-3, 7)$

2. (a) $f(x) = \begin{cases} -1 & \text{if } x < 0 \\ 1 & \text{if } x \geq 0 \end{cases}$ (b) $g(x) = \begin{cases} 3 & \text{if } x \leq -2 \\ 1 & \text{if } -2 < x \leq 1 \\ -1 & \text{if } x > 1 \end{cases}$

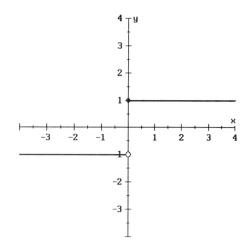 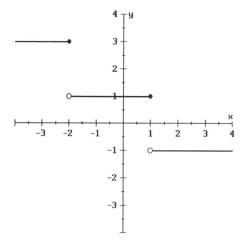

Domain: $(-\infty, +\infty)$ Domain: $(-\infty, +\infty)$

Range: $\{-1, 1\}$ Range: $\{-1, 1, 3\}$

(c) $y = |x|$

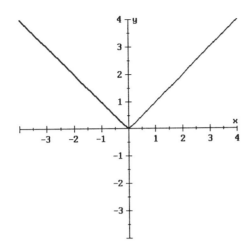

Domain: $(-\infty, +\infty)$

Range: $[0, +\infty)$

(d) $y = [\![x]\!]$

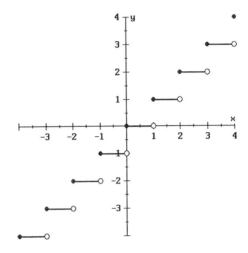

Domain: $(-\infty, +\infty)$

Range: set of integers

(e) $f(x) = \dfrac{|x|}{x}$

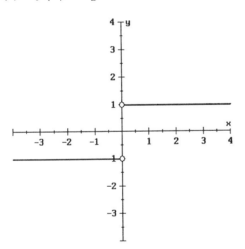

Domain: $(-\infty, 0) \cup (0 + \infty)$

Range: $\{-1, 1\}$

(f) $f = \{(1,2), (2,1), 3, -1)\}$

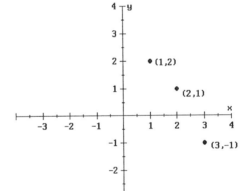

Domain: $\{1, 2, 3\}$

Range: $\{-1, 1, 2\}$

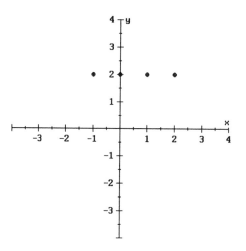

(g)

$h = \{(-1, 2), (0, 2), (1, 2), (2, 2)\}$

Domain: $\{-1, 0, 1, 2\}$

Range: $\{2\}$

Exercise III

1. (a) $f(2) = 3$, $f(0) = 1$, $f(-1) = 0$, $f(x+h) = x+h+1$,

   $f(x+1) = x+2$, $f(2x) = 2x+1$,

   $f(f(x)) = f(x+1) = x+1+1 = x+2$

   (b) $f(2) = 5$, $f(0) = 1$, $f(-1) = 2$,

   $f(x+h) = (x+h)^2 + 1 = x^2 + 2xh + h^2 + 1$,

   $f(x+1) = (x+1)^2 + 1 = x^2 + 2x + 2$, $f(2x) = (2x)^2 + 1 = 4x^2 + 1$,

   $f(f(x)) = f(x^2 + 1) = (x^2 + 1)^2 + 1 = x^4 + 2x^2 + 2$

   (c) $f(2) = \sqrt{2}$, $f(0) = 0$, $f(-1)$ not defined,

   $f(x+h) = \sqrt{x+h}$ if $x+h \geq 0$,

   $f(x+1) = \sqrt{x+1}$ if $x \geq -1$, $\qquad f(2x) = \sqrt{2x}$ if $x \geq 0$,

   $f(f(x)) = f(\sqrt{x}) = \sqrt{\sqrt{x}} = (x^{\frac{1}{2}})^{\frac{1}{2}} = x^{\frac{1}{4}}$ if $x \geq 0$

   (d) $f(2) = 9$, $f(0) = 1$, $f(-1) = 0$,

   $f(x+h) = (x+h)^3 + 1 = x^3 + 3x^2 h + 3xh^2 + 2$,

   $f(x+1) = (x+1)^3 + 1 = x^3 + 3x^2 + 3x + 2$,

   $f(2x) = (2x)^3 + 1 = 8x^3 + 1$, $f(f(x)) = f(x^3 + 1) = x^9 + 3x^6 + 3x^3 + 2$

2.   (a)   Domain $(f) = (-\infty, +\infty)$ (b)   Domain $(f) = [0, +\infty)$

    (c) $g(x) = \sqrt{x-7}$ real $\Leftrightarrow x - 7 \geq 0 \Leftrightarrow x \geq 7 \Leftrightarrow$ Domain $(g) = [7, +\infty)$

    (d) $h(x) = \dfrac{x}{x^2 - 1}$, $x^2 - 1 = 0 \Leftrightarrow x = \pm 1$

        Domain $(h) = (-\infty, -1) \cup (-1, 1) \cup (1, +\infty) = \{x \mid x \text{ real}, \ x \neq \pm 1\}$

    (e) $P(x) = \dfrac{\sqrt{x}}{x^2 - 1}$, $\sqrt{x}$ real $\Leftrightarrow x \geq 0$ and $x^2 - 1 = 0 \Leftrightarrow x = \pm 1$

        Recall   Domain $\left(\dfrac{f}{g}\right) = \{x \mid x \in$ Domain $(f) \cap$ Domain $(g), \ g(x) \neq 0\}$

        Domain $(P) = [0, 1) \cup (1, +\infty)$

    (f) $H(x) = \dfrac{\sqrt{x-3}}{\sqrt{x+3}} = \dfrac{f(x)}{g(x)} \Rightarrow$ Domain $(f) = [3, +\infty)$ and

        Domain $(g) = [-3, +\infty)$

        Recall   Domain $\left(\dfrac{f}{g}\right) = \{x \mid x \in$ Domain $(f) \cap$ Domain $(g), \ g(x) \neq 0\}$

        Domain $(H) = [3, +\infty)$

3.   Recall for functions f and g with respective domains Domain (f) and Domain (g)

    that

    Domain$(f + g) =$ Domain $(f - g) =$ Domain $(fg) =$ Domain $(f) \cap$ Domain (g),

    Domain $\left(\dfrac{f}{g}\right) = \{x \mid x \in$ Domain $(f) \cap$ Domain $(g), \ g(x) \neq 0\}$,

    Domain $\left(\dfrac{g}{f}\right) = \{x \mid x \in$ Domain $(g) \cap$ Domain $(f), \ f(x) \neq 0\}$,

    Domain $\left(\dfrac{1}{f}\right) = \{x \mid x \in$ Domain $(f), \ f(x) \neq 0\}$,

(a) $f(x) = x + 3,$ Domain $(f) = (-\infty, +\infty);$

$g(x) = x^2 + 2,$ Domain $(g) = (-\infty, +\infty).$

$(f + g)(x) = x^2 + x + 5,$ Domain $(f + g) = (-\infty, +\infty);$

$(f - g)(x) = -x^2 + x + 1,$ Domain $(f - g) = (-\infty, +\infty);$

$(fg)(x) = (x + 3)(x^2 + 2) = x^3 + 3x^2 + 2x + 6,$

                     Domain $(fg) = (-\infty, +\infty);$

$\left(\dfrac{f}{g}\right)(x) = \dfrac{x + 3}{x^2 + 2},$ Domain $\left(\dfrac{f}{g}\right) = (-\infty, +\infty);$

$\left(\dfrac{g}{f}\right)(x) = \dfrac{x^2 + 2}{x + 3},$ Domain $\left(\dfrac{g}{f}\right) = (-\infty, -3) \cup (-3, +\infty);$

$(-f)(x) = -x - 3,$ Domain $(-f) = (-\infty, +\infty);$

$\left(\dfrac{1}{f}\right)(x) = \dfrac{1}{x + 3},$ Domain $\left(\dfrac{1}{f}\right) = (-\infty, -3) \cup (-3, +\infty).$

(b) $f(x) = 2x + 1,$ Domain $(f) = (-\infty, +\infty);$

$g(x) = \sqrt{x + 1},$ Domain $(g) = [-1, +\infty).$

$(f + g)(x) = 2x + 1 + \sqrt{x + 1},$ Domain $(f + g) = [-1, +\infty);$

$(f - g)(x) = 2x + 1 - \sqrt{x + 1},$ Domain $(f - g) = [-1, +\infty);$

$(fg)(x) = (2x + 1)(\sqrt{x + 1}),$ Domain $(fg) = [-1, +\infty);$

$\left(\dfrac{f}{g}\right)(x) = \dfrac{2x + 1}{\sqrt{x + 1}},$ Domain $\left(\dfrac{f}{g}\right) = (-1, +\infty);$

$\left(\dfrac{g}{f}\right)(x) = \dfrac{\sqrt{x + 1}}{2x + 1},$ Domain $\left(\dfrac{g}{f}\right) = [-1, -\dfrac{1}{2}) \cup (-\dfrac{1}{2}, +\infty);$

$(-f)(x) = -2x - 1,$ Domain $(-f) = (-\infty, +\infty);$

$\left(\dfrac{1}{f}\right)(x) = \dfrac{1}{2x + 1},$ Domain $\left(\dfrac{1}{f}\right) = (-\infty, -\dfrac{1}{2}) \cup (-\dfrac{1}{2}, +\infty).$

(c) $f(x) = x,$ Domain $(f) = (-\infty, +\infty);$

$g(x) = x^2 - 1,$ Domain $(g) = (-\infty, +\infty).$

$(f + g)(x) = x^2 + x - 1,$ Domain $(f + g) = (-\infty, +\infty);$

$$(f-g)(x) = -x^2 + x + 1, \qquad \text{Domain}\,(f-g) = (-\infty, +\infty);$$

$$(fg)(x) = x^3 - x, \qquad \text{Domain}\,(fg) = (-\infty, +\infty);$$

$$\left(\frac{f}{g}\right)(x) = \frac{x}{x^2-1}, \quad \text{Domain}\left(\frac{f}{g}\right) = (-\infty, -1) \cup (-1, 1) \cup (1, +\infty);$$

$$\left(\frac{g}{f}\right)(x) = \frac{x^2-1}{x}, \qquad \text{Domain}\left(\frac{g}{f}\right) = (-\infty, 0) \cup (0, +\infty);$$

$$(-f)(x) = -x, \qquad \text{Domain}\,(-f) = (-\infty, +\infty);$$

$$\left(\frac{1}{f}\right)(x) = \frac{1}{x}, \qquad \text{Domain}\left(\frac{1}{f}\right) = (-\infty, 0) \cup (0, +\infty).$$

(d) $f = \{(2,4),(3,9),(4,6),(5,7)\},$ Domain $(f) = \{2,3,4,5\};$

$g = \{(2,2),(3,3),(4,2),(5,1)\},$ Domain $(g) = \{2,3,4,5\}.$

$f+g = \{(2,6),(3,12),(4,8),(5,8)\},$ Domain $(f+g) = \{2,3,4,5\};$

$f-g = \{(2,2),(3,6),(4,4),(5,6)\},$ Domain $(f-g) = \{2,3,4,5\};$

$fg = \{(2,8),(3,27),(4,12),(5,7)\},$ Domain $(fg) = \{2,3,4,5\};$

$\dfrac{f}{g} = \{(2,2),(3,3),(4,3),(5,7)\},$ Domain $(\frac{f}{g}) = \{2,3,4,5\};$

$\dfrac{g}{f} = \{(2,\frac{1}{2}),(3,\frac{1}{3}),(4,\frac{1}{3}),(5,\frac{1}{7})\},$ Domain $(\frac{g}{f}) = \{2,3,4,5\};$

$-f = \{(2,-4),(3,-9),(4,-6),(5,-7)\},$

   Domain $(-f) = \{2,3,4,5\};$

$\dfrac{1}{f} = \{(2,\frac{1}{4}),(3,\frac{1}{9}),(4,\frac{1}{6}),(5,\frac{1}{7})\},$ Domain $(\frac{1}{f}) = \{2,3,4,5\}.$

(e) $f = \{(1,3),(2,2),(3,-1),(4,0)\},$ Domain $(f) = \{1,2,3,4\};$

$g = \{(1,0),(3,4),(4,-1)\},$ Domain $(g) = \{1,3,4\}.$

$f+g = \{(1,3),(3,3),(4,-1)\},$ Domain $(f+g) = \{1,3,4\};$

$f-g = \{(1,3),(3,-5),(4,1)\},$ Domain $(f-g) = \{1,3,4\};$

$fg = \{(1,0),(3,-4),(4,0)\},$ Domain $(fg) = \{1,3,4\};$

$$\frac{f}{g} = \{(3, \frac{-1}{4}), (4, 0)\}, \qquad \text{Domain}\left(\frac{f}{g}\right) = \{3, 4\};$$

$$\frac{g}{f} = \{(1, 0), (3, -4)\}, \qquad \text{Domain}\left(\frac{g}{f}\right) = \{1, 3\};$$

$$-f = \{(1, -3), (2, -2), (3, 1), (4, 0)\}, \quad \text{Domain}(-f) = \{1, 2, 3, 4\}.$$

Exercise IV

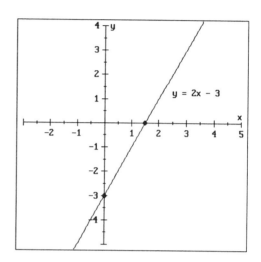

1. (a) $y = mx + b$

     slope $m = 2$ and y-intercept $b = -3$

     equation of the line is $y = 2x - 3$

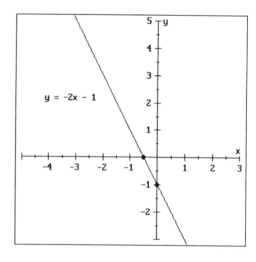

   (b)   Use slope-point equation

      $y - y_1 = m(x - x_1)$ where

      $m = -2$ and $(x_1, y_1) = (2, -5)$

      Hence we have $y - (-5) = -2(x - 2)$

      which we rewrite as $y = -2x - 1$

(c) Use the two point equation

$$y - y_1 = \left(\frac{y_2 - y_1}{x_2 - x_1}\right)(x - x_1) \text{ where}$$

$$(x_1, y_1) = (-3, 4) \text{ and } (x_2, y_2) = (5, -2)$$

This yields $y - 4 = \left(\dfrac{-2 - 4}{5 - (-3)}\right)(x - (-3))$

$$\Rightarrow \ y - 4 = -\frac{3}{4}(x + 3) \ \Rightarrow \ y = -\frac{3}{4}x + \frac{7}{4}$$

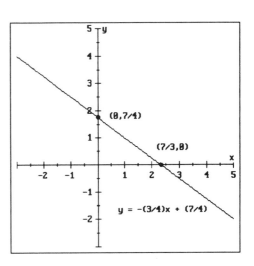

2. (a) Solve for y: $5y = 3x + 6 \ \Rightarrow \ y = \dfrac{3}{5}x + \dfrac{6}{5}$ which, from the slope-intercept

form, indicates that the slope $m = \dfrac{3}{5}$ and the y-intercept $b = \dfrac{6}{5}$.

(b) Solve for y: $7y = 2x + 1 \ \Rightarrow \ y = \dfrac{2}{7}x + \dfrac{1}{7}$ which, from the slope-intercept

form, indicates that the slope $m = \dfrac{2}{7}$ and the y-intercept $b = \dfrac{1}{7}$.

(c) Solve for y: $y = -x$ which indicates that the slope $m = -1$ and the y-intercept $b = 0$.

(d) Solve for y: $2y = -3x + 2 \ \Rightarrow \ y = -\dfrac{3}{2}x + 1$, which, from the slope-intercept form, indicates that the slope $m = -\dfrac{3}{2}$ and the y-intercept $b = 1$.

3. (a) $y = x^2$

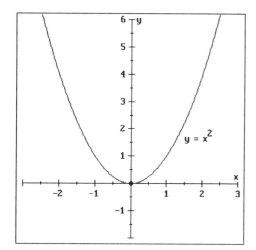

Domain: $(-\infty, +\infty)$

Range: $[0, +\infty)$

(b)(i) $y = -x^2$

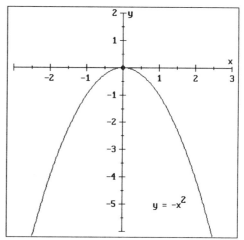

Domain: $(-\infty, +\infty)$

Range: $(-\infty, 0]$

3. (b)(ii) $y = x^2 + 2$

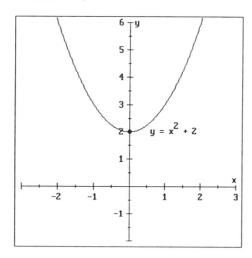

Domain: $(-\infty, +\infty)$

Range: $[2, +\infty)$

(b)(iii) $y = x^2 - 2$

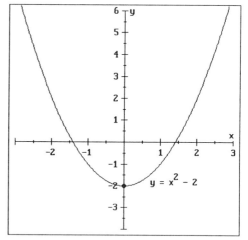

Domain: $(-\infty, +\infty)$

Range: $[-2, +\infty)$

3. (b)(iv) $y = (x-2)^2$ (b)(v) $y = (x+2)^2$

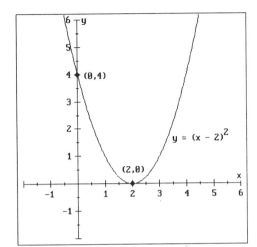 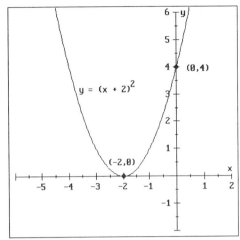

Domain: $(-\infty, +\infty)$ Domain: $(-\infty, +\infty)$

Range: $[0, +\infty)$ Range: $[0, +\infty)$

3. (b)(vi) $y = 2x^2$ (b)(vii) $y = \frac{1}{2}x^2$

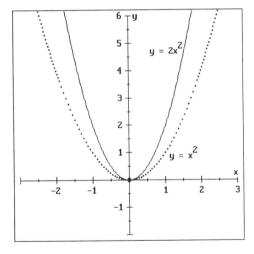 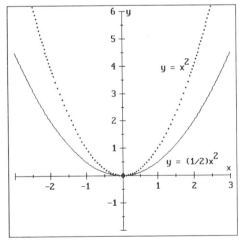

Domain: $(-\infty, +\infty)$ Domain: $(-\infty, +\infty)$

Range: $[0, +\infty)$ Range: $[0, +\infty)$

3. (c) (i) $y = x^2 + 3$ (c) (ii) $y = x^2 - 3$

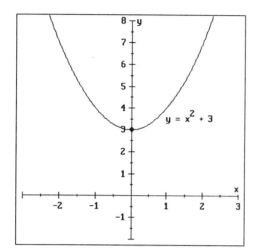 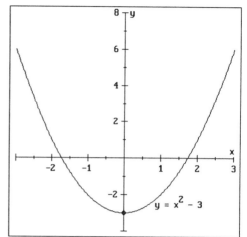

Domain: $(-\infty, +\infty)$ Domain: $(-\infty, +\infty)$

Range: $[3, +\infty)$ Range: $[-3, +\infty)$

3. (c) (iii) $y = (x - 3)^2$ (c) (iv) $y = (x + 3)^2$

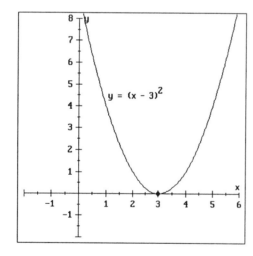 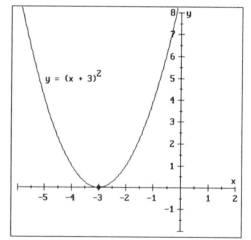

Domain: $(-\infty, +\infty)$ Domain: $(-\infty, +\infty)$

Range: $[0, +\infty)$ Range: $[0, +\infty)$

3. (c) (v) $y = -x^2 + 1$ (c) (vi) $y = -x^2 - 2$

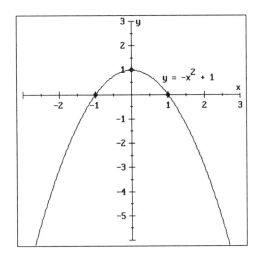   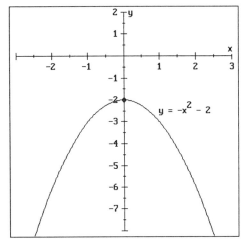

Domain: $(-\infty, +\infty)$ Domain: $(-\infty, +\infty)$

Range: $(-\infty, 1]$ Range: $(-\infty, -2]$

3. (c) (vii) $y = (x - 1)^2 + 3$ (c) (viii) $y = -2(x - 2)^2 - 1$

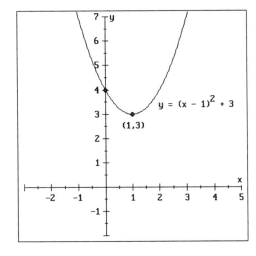   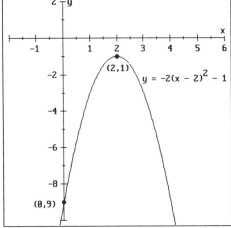

Domain: $(-\infty, +\infty)$ Domain: $(-\infty, +\infty)$

Range: $[3, +\infty)$ Range: $(-\infty, -1]$

4.   (*i*) upwards   (*ii*) downwards   (*iii*) right   (*iv*) left   (*v*) reflected

5. (a) $y = f(x)$ $y = f(x - 1)$ $y = f(x + 2)$

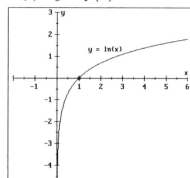
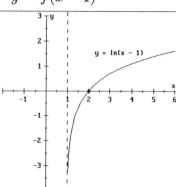
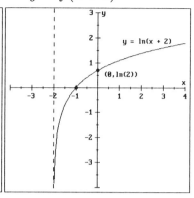

$f(x)$ in this case is $y = ln(x)$ $y = ln(x - 1)$ $y = ln(x + 2)$

5. (b) $y = g(x)$ $y = g(x) + 2$ $y = g(x) - 1$

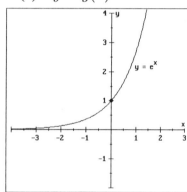
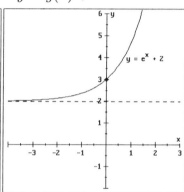
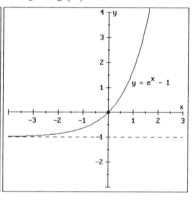

$g(x)$ in this case is $y = e^x$ $y = e^x + 2$ $y = e^x - 1$

5. (c) $y = h(x)$ $y = -h(x) + 1$ $y = h(x - 1) - 2$

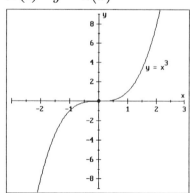
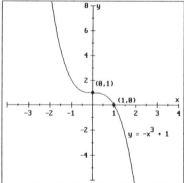
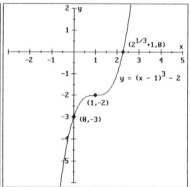

$h(x)$ in this case is $y = x^3$ $y = -x^3 + 1$ $y = (x - 1)^3 - 2$

6. (a)

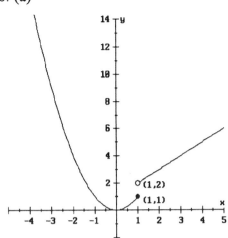

Range: $[0, +\infty)$

(b)

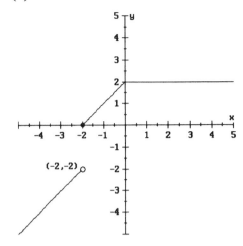

Range: $(-\infty, -2) \cup [0, 2]$

6. (c)

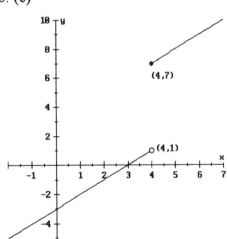

Range: $(-\infty, 1) \cup [7, +\infty)$

(d)

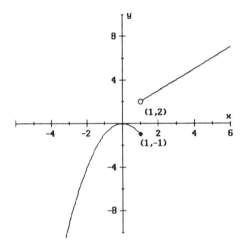

Range: $(-\infty, 0] \cup (2, +\infty)$

SOLUTIONS FOR LAB 1

PART B. Supplementary Problems

1. $y = \dfrac{x}{|x|}$

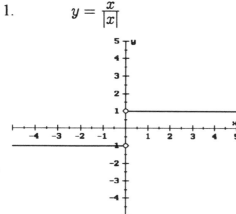

Domain $= (-\infty, 0) \cup (0, +\infty)$
Range $= \{-1, 1\}$

2. $y = \dfrac{|x|}{x}$

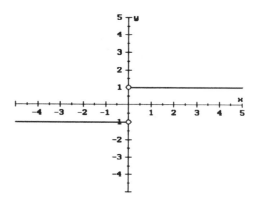

Domain $= (-\infty, 0) \cup (0, +\infty)$
Range $= \{-1, 1\}$

3. $y = x + |x|$

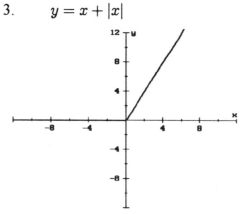

Domain $= (-\infty, +\infty)$
Range $= [0, +\infty)$

4. $y = x - |x|$

Domain $= (-\infty, +\infty)$
Range $= (-\infty, 0]$

5. $y = x|x|$

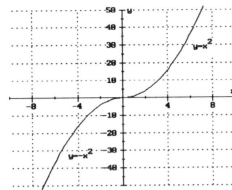

Domain $= (-\infty, +\infty)$
Range $= (-\infty, +\infty)$

6. $y = x + [\![x]\!]$

Domain $= (-\infty, +\infty)$
Range $= \{y | y \in [2n, 2n+1), n = 0, \pm 1, \pm 2, ...\}$

7. $y = x - [\![x]\!]$

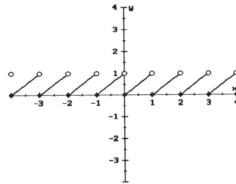

Domain $= (-\infty, +\infty)$
Range $= [0, 1)$

SOLUTIONS FOR LAB **2**

PART B. Supplementary Problems

1. (a) $y = |x - 3| - 2$ (b) $y = [\![x]\!] - x$

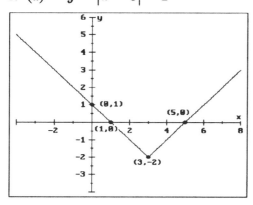 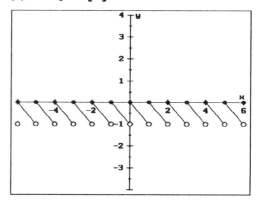

Domain = $(-\infty, +\infty)$ Domain = $(-\infty, +\infty)$

Range = $[-2, +\infty)$ Range = $(-1, 0]$

(c) $f(x) = \begin{cases} x^2 & \text{if } x \le 0 \\ x - 1 & \text{if } x > 0 \end{cases}$

Domain: $(-\infty, +\infty)$

Range: $(-1, +\infty)$

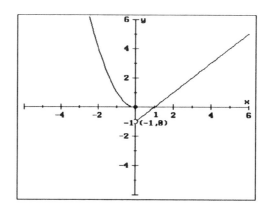

2. (a) $y = -2x^2 + 12x - 15$

   $\qquad = -2(x^2 - 6) - 15$

   $\qquad = -2(x^2 - 6x + 9 - 9) - 15$

   $\qquad = -2(x^2 - 6x + 9) + 18 - 15$

   $\qquad = -2(x - 3)^2 + 3$

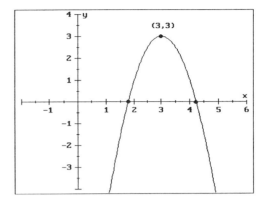

The maximum value of 3 occurs at $x = 3$.

2. (b) $y = \frac{1}{4}(x^2+6x+1)$

   $\qquad = \frac{1}{4}(x^2+6x+9 - 8)$

   $\qquad = \frac{1}{4}(x^2+6x+9) - 2$

   $\qquad = \frac{1}{4}(x + 3)^2 - 2$

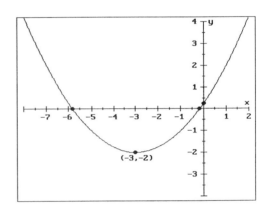

The minimum value of -2 occurs at x $= -3$.

3.   To have a maximum value of -20 at x $= 2$ the quadratic function must be of the form y $= c(x - 2)^2 - 20$ where c < 0. Therefore (C) $-3(x - 2)^2 - 20$ is the answer.

4.   Let a denote the percent in Option A and let b denote the percent in Option B. Hence the model functions for the two options becomes:

$$A(x) = 1{,}000 + .01ax \quad \text{and} \quad B(x) = \begin{cases} 1{,}300 & \text{if } x \le 15{,}000 \\ 1{,}300 + .01b(x - 15{,}000) & \text{if } x > 15{,}0000 \end{cases}$$

In other words we need to find the values of a and b so that the graphs of the two functions intersect at x $= 6{,}000$ and x $= 37{,}500$; i.e., find a and b such that

   (i)   A(6,000) = B(6,000) and
   (ii)   A(37,500) = B(37,500).

For (i)

$A(6,000) = B(6,000)$

$1,000 + .01a(6,000) = 1,300$

$60a=300 \quad \Rightarrow \quad a = 5$.   The percent in Option A is 5%.

For (ii) using $a = 5$

$A(37,500) = B(37,500)$

$1,000 + .01(5)(37,500) = 1,300 + .01b(37,500 - 15,000)$

$1,000 + 1,875 = 1,300 + 225b$

$1575 = 225b \quad \Rightarrow \quad b = 7$.   The percent in Option B is 7%.

5.(i)   Let t denote the time in days and let I(t) denote the number of people infected a time t. The quadratic model is given by $I(t) = c(t - b)^2 + c$. Since the model is a quadratic function and $I(0) = 0$ and $I(40) = 0$ then the maximum occurs at the midpoint between $t = 0$ and $t = 40$, i.e. $t = 20$. Therefore $b = 20$ and $a = 800$ and we know that c must be negative (c<0).

Hence $I(0) = c(0 - 20)^2+800 = 0 \Rightarrow 400c = -800 \Rightarrow c = -2$. The required model is $I(t) = -2(t - 20)^2+800$.

(ii)   The number of people infected at day $t = 30$ is $I(30) = -2(30 - 20)^2+800 = 600$.

SOLUTIONS FOR LAB 3

PART B. Supplementary Problems

1.   Given f(x) = $log(x - 1) + 2$.   Since we are shifting the graph of f 3 units to the left
      and then shifting it down 3 units the required function has the form
      $$y = f(x+3) - 3 = (log((x+3) - 1) + 2) - 3 = log(x+2) - 1.$$

2. $2\,log_3(2) + log_3(x+1) = log_3(x+8)$
   $$\Leftrightarrow\quad log_3(2^2) + log_3(x+1) - log_3(x+8) = 0$$

   $$\Leftrightarrow\quad log_3\left(\frac{4(x+1)}{(x+8)}\right) = 0$$

   $$\Leftrightarrow\quad \left(\frac{4x+4}{x+8}\right) = 3^0 = 1$$

   $$\Leftrightarrow\quad 4x+4 = x+8 \quad\Leftrightarrow\quad x = \frac{4}{3}$$

3.   Let $y = f(x) = 3e^{2x} - 5$.   Since f is a 1-1 function the $x = f^{-1}(y)$
      Solve for x in terms of y: $y = 3e^{2x} - 5 \Leftrightarrow y+5 = 3e^{2x} \Leftrightarrow \dfrac{y+5}{3} = e^{2x}$

      $\Leftrightarrow\ ln(\dfrac{y+5}{3}) = ln(e^{2x}) = 2x \Leftrightarrow x = \dfrac{1}{2}\,ln(\dfrac{y+5}{3}) = f^{-1}(y)$.

      Therefore $f^{-1}(x) = \dfrac{1}{2}\,ln(\dfrac{x+5}{3})$.

4. (a) $y = log(|x|)$ (b) $y = log_2([\![x]\!])$ for $1 \le x < 3$

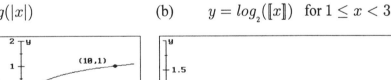

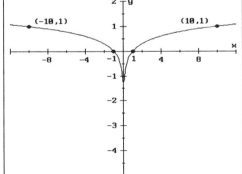

Domain = $(-\infty, 0) \cup (0, +\infty)$ Domain = $[1, 3)$

Range = $(-\infty, +\infty)$ Range = $\{0, 1\}$

$y = [\![log_4(x)]\!]$ for $\frac{1}{4} \le x < 4$

4. (c)

Domain: $[\frac{1}{4}. 4)$

Range: $\{-1, 0\}$

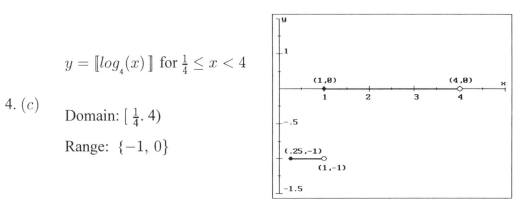

5   The general model is $A(t) = A_0 e^{kt}$ where

        $A(t)$: the amount present at time t

        A_0 : the initial amount, i.e. the amount at t=0

        k: the growth rate constant (k>0)

        t: time (in minutes)

We are told that (i) at t = 0, $A(0) = A_0 = 1,000$

      (ii) at t = 12, $A(12) = 2,000$

      (iii) find t = ? when $A(t) = 1,000,000$.

We must first find the growth rate constant k at t = 12

$$A(12) = 2,000 = 1,000 e^{k(12)} \quad \Leftrightarrow \quad 2 = e^{12k}$$

(taking *ln* of both sides) $ln(2) = ln(e^{12k}) = 12k \Leftrightarrow k = \frac{1}{12} ln(2)$.

Hence $A(t) = 1,000 e^{\frac{1}{12} ln(2) t}$.

$$A(t) = 1,000,000 = 1,000 e^{\frac{1}{12} ln(2) t}$$

Solve for t: $1,000 = e^{\frac{1}{12} ln(2) t}$

        $\Leftrightarrow ln(1,000) = \frac{1}{12} ln(2)$ (taking *ln* of both sides)

        $\Leftrightarrow t = \frac{12 ln(1,000)}{ln(2)}$ minutes   (119.6 minutes)

6.   General model is $A(t) = A_0 e^{-kt}$ where k>0. We are given that $t_{\frac{1}{2}} = 1600$ years and $A_0 = 150$ mg. We are required to find t when $A(t) = 30$.

First we find the decay rate constant k.

$$A(1600) = \tfrac{1}{2} A_0 = \tfrac{1}{2}(150) = 150 \, e^{-k(1600)}$$

$$\Leftrightarrow \quad \tfrac{1}{2} = e^{-k(1600)}$$

$$\Leftrightarrow \quad ln(\tfrac{1}{2}) = -1600k \quad \Leftrightarrow \quad k = -\tfrac{1}{1600} ln(\tfrac{1}{2}) \ \ yr^{-1}$$

We now solve for t.

$$A(t) = 30 = 150 \, e^{-(-\frac{1}{1600} ln(\frac{1}{2}))t}$$

$$\Leftrightarrow \quad \tfrac{1}{5} = e^{-(-\frac{1}{1600} ln(\frac{1}{2}))t} \quad \Leftrightarrow \quad ln(\tfrac{1}{5}) = \tfrac{1}{1600} ln(\tfrac{1}{2}))t$$

$$\Leftrightarrow \quad t = 1600 \, \frac{ln(\frac{1}{5})}{ln(\frac{1}{2})} \ \ \text{years} \qquad (\ 3715 \ \text{years})$$

7.   General model is $A(t) = A_0 e^{-kt}$ where k>0.
We are given that $A(2) = 30$ and $A(5) = 20$.
(a)   To find the decay rate k

$$A(2) = 30 = A_0 e^{-2k} \qquad\qquad ....\boxed{1}$$
$$A(5) = 20 = A_0 \, e^{-5k} \qquad\qquad ....\boxed{2}$$

Divide equation $\boxed{1}$ by equation $\boxed{2}$

$$\frac{A_0 e^{-2k}}{A_0 e^{-5k}} = \frac{30}{20} \qquad\qquad \Rightarrow \quad e^{-2k+5k} = \frac{3}{2}$$

$$\Rightarrow \quad e^{3k} = \frac{3}{2} \quad \Rightarrow \quad 3k = ln(\tfrac{3}{2}) \quad \Rightarrow \quad k = \tfrac{1}{3} ln(\tfrac{3}{2}) \ \ hr^{-1}$$

(b)   Find $t_{\frac{1}{2}}$. Recall that this is the time such that

$$A(t_{\frac{1}{2}}) = \tfrac{1}{2}A_0. \text{ Therefore } \quad \tfrac{1}{2}A_0 = A_0 e^{-\frac{1}{3} \ln(\frac{3}{2})t_{\frac{1}{2}}}$$

$$\Leftrightarrow \quad \tfrac{1}{2} = e^{-\frac{1}{3} \ln(\frac{3}{2})t_{\frac{1}{2}}}$$

$$\Leftrightarrow \quad \ln(\tfrac{1}{2}) = -\tfrac{1}{3} \ln(\tfrac{3}{2})t_{\frac{1}{2}}$$

$$\Leftrightarrow \quad t_{\frac{1}{2}} = \frac{-3 \ln(\frac{1}{2})}{\ln(\frac{3}{2})} \text{ or } \frac{3 \ln(2)}{\ln(\frac{3}{2})} \text{ hours.}$$

(c)   Find A_0. We have $A(t) = A_0 e^{-\frac{1}{3} \ln(\frac{3}{2})t}$.

At $t = 2$, $A(2) = 30 = A_0 e^{-\frac{1}{3} \ln(\frac{3}{2})(2)} = A_0 e^{-\frac{2}{3} \ln(\frac{3}{2})}$

(Recall $r\ln(M) = \ln(M^r)$ $30 = A_0 e^{\ln(\frac{3}{2})^{-\frac{2}{3}}}$

(Recall $e^{\ln(M^r)} = M^r$) $30 = A_0(\tfrac{3}{2})^{-\frac{2}{3}} \quad \Leftrightarrow \quad A_0 = 30(\tfrac{3}{2})^{\frac{2}{3}}$ grams.

8.   General model is $A(t) = A_0 e^{-kt}$ where $k > 0$. We are told that We are told that $t_{\frac{1}{2}} = 5685$ years and we are required to find t such that $A(t) = \frac{25}{100} A_0 = \frac{1}{4}A_0$. First we must find k.

$$A(5685) = \tfrac{1}{2}A_0 = A_0 e^{-5685k}$$
$$\Leftrightarrow \quad \ln(\tfrac{1}{2}) = -5685k \quad \Leftrightarrow \quad k = \frac{-\ln(\frac{1}{2})}{5685} \text{ yrs}^{-1}$$

Now we find the required t.
$$\tfrac{1}{4}A_0 = A_0 e^{-(\frac{1}{5685} \ln(\frac{1}{2}))t} = A_0 e^{(\frac{1}{5685} \ln(\frac{1}{2}))t}$$

$$\Leftrightarrow \quad \tfrac{1}{4} = e^{(\frac{1}{5685} \ln(\frac{1}{2}))t} \quad \Leftrightarrow \quad \ln(\tfrac{1}{4}) = \frac{1}{5685} \ln(\tfrac{1}{2})t$$

$$\Leftrightarrow \quad t = 5685 \frac{\ln(\frac{1}{4})}{\ln(\frac{1}{2})} = 5685 \frac{\ln((\frac{1}{2})^2)}{\ln(\frac{1}{2})} = 5685 \frac{(2) \ln(\frac{1}{2})}{\ln(\frac{1}{2})} = 5685(2)$$

$$= 11{,}370 \text{ years.} \quad \text{Hence the specimen is } 11{,}370 \text{ years old.}$$

SOLUTIONS FOR LAB 4

PART B. Supplementary Problems

1.   Model is $y = a \cos(k\pi t - b) + c.$ Rewrite as $y = a \cos(k\pi(t - \frac{b}{k\pi})) + c.$

   Amplitude: $a = \dfrac{\text{Max - Min}}{2} = \dfrac{65 - 25}{2} = 20 \implies \boxed{a = 20}$

   Period of the model: Period $= \dfrac{2\pi}{k\pi} = 40 \implies \boxed{k = \dfrac{1}{20}}$

   At this point we have $y = 20 \cos(\frac{1}{20}\pi t).$
   Sketch the graph of this function to determine the position of the minimum.

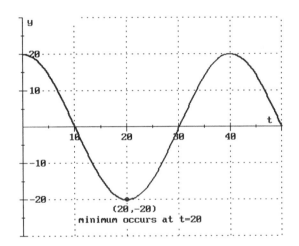

   From the graph we see that for the minimum to occur at t = 15 days we have to shift
   the graph of $y = 20 \cos(\frac{1}{20}\pi t)$ five (5) units to the left.   Therefore the model
   becomes

$$y = 20 \cos(\tfrac{1}{20}\pi(t + 5))$$

   At this point this model has all the requirements except the max-min values. The
   max-min values of this model are 20 and -20 and we require it to have 65 and 25
   respectively. In other words we have to determine the vertical shift of this function.

   The vertical shift is $\dfrac{\text{max + min}}{2} = \dfrac{65 + 25}{2} = 45.$

   Therefore the required model is

$$y = 20 \cos(\tfrac{1}{20}\pi(t + 5)) + 45$$

   or to match the original form our model:

$$y = 20 \cos(\tfrac{1}{20}\pi t - (-\tfrac{1}{4}\pi)) + 45 \text{ which yields that } \boxed{b = -\tfrac{1}{4}\pi} \text{ and } \boxed{c = 45}.$$

2.   Function   Calculations   Basic Period

     (A) $y = \cos(\frac{3}{2}x)$ $0 \le \frac{3x}{2} \le 2\pi \;\Rightarrow\; 0 \le x \le \frac{4}{3}\pi$ $\frac{4}{3}\pi$

     (B) $y = \sin(\frac{2}{3}\pi x)$ $0 \le \frac{2\pi x}{3} \le 2\pi \;\Rightarrow\; 0 \le x \le 3$ 3

     (C) $y = \cos(\frac{1}{3}\pi x)$ $0 \le \frac{1x}{3} \le 2\pi \;\Rightarrow\; 0 \le x \le 6\pi$ 6π

     (D) $y = \sin(\frac{2}{3}x)$ $0 \le \frac{2x}{3} \le 2\pi \;\Rightarrow\; 0 \le x \le 3\pi$ 3π

     (E) $y = \cos(3\pi x)$ $0 \le 3\pi x \le 2\pi \;\Rightarrow\; 0 \le x \le \frac{2}{3}$ $\frac{2}{3}$

            Hence (B) $y = \sin(\frac{2}{3}\pi x)$ has basic period 3.

3.   For the graph of a function to be a straight line on semi-log graph paper it must have the general form of $y = cb^{kx}$ (an exponential function). The only functions that have this form are (A) $y = 100(2^x)$ and (C) $y = 100(4^x)$. You now check to see which has the property that, when $x = 2$, $y = 400$. (A) $y = 100(2^2) = 400$. Hence (A) is the answer.

4.   Since the graph of the required function is a straight line on log-log graph paper then the function must have the general form of an allometric function $y = cx^k$. We must determine the constants c and k.

Recall that $log(y) = log(c) + k \, log(x)$ where k is the slope of the straight line. Hence

$$\text{slope} \;\; k = \frac{log(y_2) - log(y_1)}{log(x_2) - log(x_1)} = \frac{log(6) - log(3)}{log(16) - log(4)} = \frac{0.77 - 0.47}{1.2 - 0.6}$$

$$= \frac{0.3}{0.6} = \frac{1}{2}$$

Recall that $y = c$ when $x = 1$ and hence if we were given a point on the graph of the form (1,c) we would know the value of c immediately. In this question, we must compute c. There are two methods of obtaining the value of c.

Method 1

Substitute $k = \frac{1}{2}$ and the point (4,3) in the equation

$$log(y) = log(c) + k \, log(x) \;\Rightarrow\; log(3) = log(c) + \frac{1}{2} \, log(4)$$

$$\Rightarrow \;\;\; log(3) = log(c) + log(4^{\frac{1}{2}}) \;\Rightarrow\; log(3) - log(2) = log(c)$$

$$\Rightarrow \;\;\; log(\tfrac{3}{2}) = log(c) \;\;\;\;\;\; \Rightarrow \;\;\;\;\;\;\; c = \frac{3}{2}$$

Method 2

Substitute $k = \frac{1}{2}$ and the point (4,3) in the equation $y = cx^k$

Hence: $3 = c(4)^{\frac{1}{2}} \;\Rightarrow\; 3 = 2c \;\Rightarrow\; c = \frac{3}{2}$.

The required function is $y = \frac{3}{2}x^{\frac{1}{2}}$.

LAB 5

Solutions to Termtest I

Total Marks 20 $\begin{cases} \textbf{12 marks for the multiple choice questions} \\ \textbf{8 marks for the word problems} \end{cases}$

PART I

Each question in this part has exactly one correct answer. Circle your choice.

1. If $f = \{(1, 3), (3, -1), (5, 0), (7, 2)\}$ and $g = \{(0, 3), (1, 4), (3, -2), (7, 0)\}$ then which of the following is FALSE?

   (A) $g - f = \{(1, 1), (3, -1), (7, -2)\}$
   (B) $g \circ f = \{(1, -2), (5, 3)\}$
   (C) $-f = \{(1, -3), (3, 1), (5, 0), (7, -2)\}$

   (D) $\frac{1}{g} = \{(1, \frac{1}{4}), (3, -\frac{1}{2})\}$ $\frac{1}{g} = \left\{ (0, \frac{1}{3}), (1, \frac{1}{4}), (3, -\frac{1}{2}) \right\}$

   (E) $\frac{g}{f} = \{(1, \frac{4}{3}), (3, 2), (7, 0)\}$

2. Let $f(x) = x^5 - 1$ and $g(x) = x^3$ then which of the following is FALSE?

   (A) $(g - f)(x) = x^3 - x^5 + 1$

   (B) Domain of $(\frac{g}{f}) = (-\infty, 1) \cup (1, +\infty)$

   (C) $(f \circ g)(x) = x^8 - 1$ $(f \circ g)(x) = f(g(x)) = f(x^3)$
   $= (x^3)^5 - 1 = x^{15} - 1$

   (D) $(g \circ f)(x) = (x^5 - 1)^3$

   (E) $(fg)(x) = x^8 - x^3$

3. The natural domain of $\dfrac{\ln(x+3)}{4-x^2}$ is

$\text{Dom}\,(\ln(x+3)) = (-3, +\infty)$

(A) $(-3, +\infty)$

$\text{Dom}\,(4-x^2) = (-\infty, +\infty)$

(B) $[-3, -2) \cup (-2, 2) \cup (2, +\infty)$

and $4-x^2 = 0$ for $x = -2$

(C) $(2, +\infty)$

and $x = 2$

(D) $(-3, -2) \cup (-2, 2) \cup (2, +\infty)$

(E) $(-3, 2) \cup (2, +\infty)$

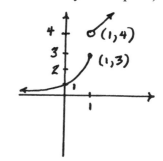

4. Let $f(x) = \begin{cases} 3^x & \text{if } x \le 1 \\ |x+3| & \text{if } x > 1 \end{cases}$.

Which of the following is the range of f?   (Hint: a sketch may be helpful.)

(A) $[0, 3) \cup [4, +\infty)$
(B) $(0, +\infty)$
(C) $(0, 3) \cup (4, +\infty)$
(D) $(-\infty, +\infty)$
(E) $(0, 3] \cup (4, +\infty)$

5. If $3e^{4x-7} = 8$ then x equals

(A) $\frac{1}{4}\ln\left(\frac{8}{3}\right) + \frac{1}{4}\ln(7)$

$3e^{4x-7} = 8$

(B) $\frac{1}{4}\left(\ln\left(\frac{8}{3}\right) + 7\right)$

$\Leftrightarrow e^{4x-7} = \frac{8}{3}$

$\Leftrightarrow \ln(e^{4x-7}) = \ln\left(\frac{8}{3}\right)$

(C) $\frac{1}{4}\ln\left(\frac{8}{3}\right) + 7$

$\Leftrightarrow 4x-7 = \ln\left(\frac{8}{3}\right)$

$\Leftrightarrow 4x = \ln\left(\frac{8}{3}\right) + 7$

(D) $4\left(\ln\left(\frac{8}{3}\right) + 7\right)$

$\Leftrightarrow x = \frac{1}{4}\left(\ln\left(\frac{8}{3}\right) + 7\right)$

(E) $\frac{1}{4}\left(\ln(8) - 7\right)$

6. Suppose in a certain lake, the bass population size, B, is given by

$B(n) = 40 + \sqrt{\dfrac{n}{120}}$ where n is the minnow population size. The minnow

population size is given by $n(p) = 2p + 3$ where p is the amount of plankton in the lake. The bass population size B as a function of the plankton p is given by

(A) $83 + 2\sqrt{\dfrac{p}{120}}$

(B) $40 + 2\sqrt{\dfrac{p+3}{120}}$

(C) $80p + 120 + \sqrt{\dfrac{p}{120}}$

(D) $40 + \sqrt{\dfrac{2p+3}{120}}$

(E) $40 + 2\sqrt{\dfrac{p}{120}}$

$B(n(p)) = B(2p+3) = 40 + \sqrt{\dfrac{2p+3}{120}}$

7. Let $f(x) = \frac{1}{3}(x-5)^{\frac{1}{3}} + 4$. The inverse function f^{-1} is given by $f^{-1}(x)$ equals

(A) $(3x-4)^3 + 5$

(B) $3(x-4)^3 + 5$

(C) $27(x-5)^3 + 8$

(D) $27x^3 + 1$

(E) $27(x-4)^3 + 5$

Let $y = \frac{1}{3}(x-5)^{\frac{1}{3}} + 4$

$\Leftrightarrow y - 4 = \frac{1}{3}(x-5)^{1/3}$

$\Leftrightarrow 3(y-4) = (x-5)^{1/3}$

$\Leftrightarrow x - 5 = 3^3(y-4)^3 = 27(y-4)^3$

$\Leftrightarrow x = 27(y-4)^3 + 5$

$\therefore f^{-1}(x) = 27(x-4)^3 + 5$

8. If $2\log_7(10x) - \log_7(25) = 2$ then x equals

(A) $\dfrac{35}{2}$

(B) $\dfrac{7}{2}$

(C) $\pm\dfrac{35}{2}$

(D) $\pm\dfrac{7}{2}$

(E) $\dfrac{245}{4}$

$\log_7\left((10x)^2\right) - \log_7(25) = 2$

$\Leftrightarrow \log_7\left(\dfrac{100x^2}{25}\right) = 2 \Leftrightarrow \dfrac{100x^2}{25} = 7^2$

$\Leftrightarrow 4x^2 = 49 \Leftrightarrow x^2 = \dfrac{49}{4}$

$\Leftrightarrow x = \pm\dfrac{7}{2}$

$x = -\dfrac{7}{2}$ inadmissible

$\therefore x = \dfrac{7}{2}$

9. The basic period of $y = 7\cos(5\pi x - 5) + 11$ is

(A) $10\pi^2$

(B) $\dfrac{2}{5}$

(C) 10

(D) $\dfrac{2}{5}\pi$

(E) $\dfrac{5}{2}$

$B.P. = \dfrac{2\pi}{5\pi} = \dfrac{2}{5}$

10. Which one of the following equations represents the sketched graph?

(A) $f(x) = -\dfrac{1}{2}x + 4$

(B) $f(x) = \dfrac{1}{16}(x-8)^2$

(C) $f(x) = (x-8)^{\frac{2}{3}}$

(D) $f(x) = (x-8)^3$

(E) $f(x) = 8e^x - 4$

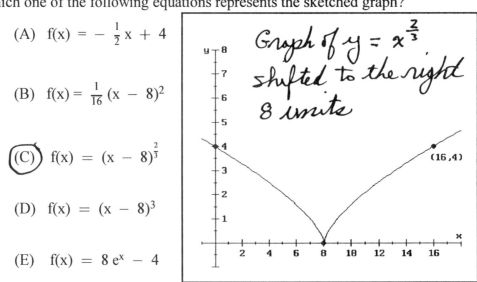

Graph of $y = x^{\frac{2}{3}}$ shifted to the right 8 units

(16,4)

11. Which of the following has a graph that is the graph of $f(x) = \sin(x+2) - 2$ shifted to the right 4 units and then shifted upwards 3?

(A) $y = \sin(x - 4) + 3$

(B) $y = \sin(x - 2) + 1$

(C) $y = \sin(x - 2) - 5$

(D) $y = \sin(x+6) + 1$

(E) $y = \sin(x+6) - 5$

$y = f(x-4) + 3$

$\quad = \Big(\sin\big((x-4)+2\big) - 2\Big) + 3$

$\quad = \sin(x-2) + 1$

12. Which of the following equations passes through the point (8, 3200) and when plotted on semi-log graph paper yields a <u>straight line</u>?

(A) $y = 800\left(\frac{1}{2}\right)^x$

(B) $y = 1600\,(2)^{\frac{x}{4}}$

(C) $y = 10x + 3120$

(D) $y = 800\, x^{\frac{2}{3}}$

(E) $y = 100\,(2)^{\frac{5x}{8}}$

Has general form $y = c\, b^{kx}$

(B) + (E) have that form.

check given values:

(B) for $x = 8$, $y = 1600\,(2)^{\frac{8}{4}} = 1600(2)^2$

$\quad = 6400 \neq 3200$

(E) $y = 100\,(2)^{\frac{5(8)}{8}} = 100\,(2)^5$

$\quad = 3200$ ✓

PART II
Work each problem. Show all your work in the space provided.
13. Sketch the graphs of the following functions on the associated axis and for the
    indicated x's. Label at least two points on each graph.

2

(A) $y = 4 \sin(\frac{\pi}{2}x - \pi)$ for $-4 \le x \le 5$

Rewrite: $y = 4\sin\left(\frac{\pi}{2}(x-2)\right)$

$B.P. = \frac{2\pi}{\frac{\pi}{2}} = 4$

∴ Graph is graph of $y = \sin\left(\frac{\pi}{2}x\right)$
  — Shifted to the
    right 2 units

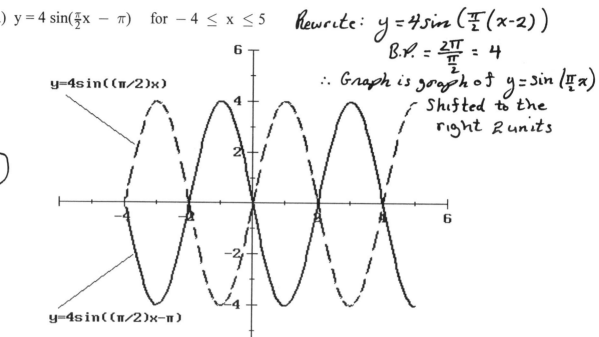

(B) $y = 2^{[x]}$ for $-1 \le x < 3$ (where $[x]$ is the greatest integer of x)

For $-1 \le x < 0$, $[x] = -1 \Rightarrow 2^{-1} = \frac{1}{2}$

$0 \le x < 1$, $[x] = 0$, $y = 2^0 = 1$

$1 \le x < 2$, $[x] = 1$, $y = 2^1 = 2$

$2 \le x < 3$, $[x] = 2$, $y = 2^2 = 4$

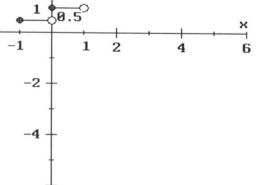

14. A pulsating light pulses so that the strength of the light emitted in one pulse is a quadratic function of time. Suppose that one pulse lasts 60 seconds and that the light strength at the beginning and end of each pulse is 0 candles. Express the light strength over one pulse as a function of time, given that the maximum strength in each pulse is 300 candles.

☒ Let $I(t)$ denote light strength at time t.

MODEL: quadratic f'n $I(t) = C(t-B)^2 + A$ —— (½)

From the graph we see that max of 300 occurs at $t = 30$

∴ $\boxed{B = 30}$ —— (½)

and $\boxed{A = 300}$ —— (½)

Hence $I(t) = C(t-30)^2 + 300$

Solve for C: $I(0) = 0 = C(0-30)^2 + 300$

⟹ $900\,C = -300$

⟹ $\boxed{C = -\frac{1}{3}}$ —— (½)

∴ $I(t) = -\frac{1}{3}(t-30)^2 + 300$

15. Area $-$ Species Curve   It has been found that the number of species S of a given taxon on an island is an allometric function of the area A of that island, $S = c(A)^k$. If research data indicates that the graph of this function is a straight line on log $-$ log graph paper passing through the points corresponding to $(A, S) = (1, 2.8)$ and $(A, S) = (100, 70.3)$ then determine the following: NOTE: USE $\log (2.8) = 0.45$ and $\log (70.3) = 1.85$

2

(i) the constant c

$$\text{Since} \quad (A, S) = (1, 2.8) \Rightarrow \boxed{C = 2.8}$$

①

(ii) the constant k $(A_1, S_1) = (1, 2.8) \ , \ (A_2, S_2) = (100, 70.3)$

Slope of line: $\quad k = \dfrac{\log (S_2) - \log (S_1)}{\log (A_2) - \log (A_1)}$

$$= \dfrac{\log (70.3) - \log (2.8)}{\log (100) - \log (1)}$$

$$= \dfrac{1.85 - 0.45}{2 - 0} \quad = .7$$

①

$$\therefore \quad \boxed{k = .7}$$

$$\text{and} \quad S = 2.8 \, A^{0.7}$$

16. The fallout from a nuclear explosion contaminated a Pacific Ocean island with the radioactive component Strontium-90, which has a half − life of 28 years. Readings from the island indicated that the level of Strontium-90 was 20 times the level considered safe for human habitation.

2

(i) State the model equation describing the Strontium-90 level as a function of time.

$$A(t) = A_0 e^{-kt} \qquad — \left(\tfrac{1}{2}\right)$$

(ii) What is the decay factor k of Strontium 90?

$$t_{\frac{1}{2}} = 28 \Rightarrow A(28) = \tfrac{1}{2} A_0 = A_0 e^{-28k}$$
$$\Leftrightarrow \tfrac{1}{2} = e^{-28k} \quad \Leftrightarrow \quad -28k = \ln\left(\tfrac{1}{2}\right)$$
$$\Leftrightarrow k = -\tfrac{1}{28} \ln\left(\tfrac{1}{2}\right) \quad \left[\text{or } \tfrac{1}{28} \ln(2) \right]$$
$$\qquad\qquad \left(\tfrac{1}{2}\right)$$

(ii) How long after the contamination will the island become safe for human habitation?

Let S denote the safe level
∴ initial amount: $A_0 = 20S$
and $A(t) = 20 S e^{\frac{1}{28} \ln\left(\frac{1}{2}\right) t}$

Find t so that $A(t) = S = 20S e^{\frac{1}{28} \ln\left(\frac{1}{2}\right) t} \qquad — \left(\tfrac{1}{2}\right)$

$$\Leftrightarrow \tfrac{1}{20} = e^{\frac{1}{28} \ln\left(\frac{1}{2}\right) t} \quad \Leftrightarrow \quad \ln\left(\tfrac{1}{20}\right) = \tfrac{1}{28} \ln\left(\tfrac{1}{2}\right) t$$

$$\Leftrightarrow t = \frac{28 \ln\left(\frac{1}{20}\right)}{\ln\left(\frac{1}{2}\right)} \approx 121 \text{ years}$$
$$\qquad\qquad \left(\tfrac{1}{2}\right)$$

SOLUTIONS FOR LAB 6

PART B. Supplementary Problems

1. (a)

Day	1	2	3	4	5
Dosage	3	5	7	9	11

(b) The dosage on the ith day is $3 + 2(i - 1)$. The total amount of venom is

$$\sum_{i=1}^{n}(3 + 2(i - 1)) \text{ after the } n\text{th dose.}$$

$$\sum_{i=1}^{n}(3 + 2(i - 1)) = \sum_{i=1}^{n}3 + 2\sum_{i=1}^{n}i - \sum_{i=1}^{n}2 = 3n + \frac{2n(n + 1)}{2} - 2n = n^2 + 2n$$

(c) Total venom needed:

$$\sum_{i=1}^{60}(3 + 2(i - 1)) = (60)^2 + 2(60) = 3600 + 120 = 3720$$

2. Let x_n denote the size of the culture at the nth generation.

(a) The size $x_{n+1} = x_n - 0.2x_n + 200 \quad \Rightarrow \quad x_{n+1} = 0.8x_n + 200$

(b) $a = 0.8$ and $b = 200$ and $\dfrac{b}{1 - a} = \dfrac{200}{1 - 0.8} = 1000$

$$x_n = \frac{b}{1 - a} + \left(x_0 - \frac{b}{1 - a}\right)a^n = 1000 + (2000 - 1000)(0.8)^n$$

$$\Rightarrow \quad x_n = 1000 + 1000(0.8)^n$$

(c) Eventual size:

$$\bar{x} = \lim_{n \to +\infty}(x_n) = \lim_{n \to +\infty}\left(1000 + 1000(0.8)^n\right) = 1000 + 0 = 1000$$

$$\left(= \frac{b}{1 - a} \text{ since } 0 < a = 0.8 < 1\right)$$

3. Let x_n denote the size of the buffalo herd at year n.

    We are given that $x_0 = 1000$.

    (a) <u>Method 1</u>   We compute the <u>difference</u> in numbers between x_{n+1} and x_n

    i.e. $\Delta x_n = x_{n+1} - x_n$.   Thus we consider losses and gains from one year to the next.

    <u>Loss:</u>   (20% decrease of herd size at year n) $-0.2x_n$

    <u>Gain:</u>   (80 buffalo are added) $+80$

    <u>Net difference:</u> $\Delta x_n = -0.2x_n + 80$

    or $x_{n+1} - x_n = -0.2x_n + 80$

    or $x_{n+1} = 0.8x_n + 80$

    <u>Method 2</u>   We compute the size of x_{n+1} directly from the size of x_n. We are told that we lose 20% of the herd size, hence going into year $n+1$ we have 80% of the herd size at year n (i.e. $0.8x_n$). Also, 80 buffalo are added.

    Therefore the size of the herd at year $n+1$ is: $x_{n+1} = 0.8x_n + 80$

    (b) Recall if $x_{n+1} = ax_n + b$ then $x_n = \dfrac{b}{1-a} + \left(x_0 - \dfrac{b}{1-a}\right)a^n$.

    In our case $a = 0.8$ and $b = 80$. Therefore

    $$x_n = \frac{80}{1-0.8} + \left(1000 - \frac{80}{1-0.8}\right)(0.8)^n$$

    $$x_n = 400 + 600(0.8)^n$$

    which is the size of the herd at year n.

(c)   The eventual size of the herd is:

$$\bar{x} = \lim_{n \to +\infty} x_n = \lim_{n \to +\infty} \left(400 + 600(0.8)^n \right) = 400$$

$$\left(\text{recall that} \quad \lim_{n \to +\infty} a^n = 0 \quad \text{if} \quad -1 < a < 1 \right)$$

(d)   If $-1 < a < 1$ then $\lim_{n \to +\infty} x_n = \dfrac{b}{1-a}$. We know $a = 0.8$ and we want to

find b such that $\lim_{n \to +\infty} x_n = \dfrac{b}{1 - 0.8} = 2500 \Rightarrow b = 500.$

You must add 500 buffalo each year.

4.   Let x_n denote the amount in the account at the end of year n.

(a)   <u>Method 1</u>

We start with amount x_n and we will compute the amount x_{n+1}

Start	x_n
\$10 service charge	$x_n - 10$
Remaining amount (increased by 5% (i.e. $\times 1.05$))	$1.05(x_n - 10)$

Therefore the value of x_{n+1} is: $x_{n+1} = 1.05(x_n - 10) = 1.05x_n - 10.5$

<u>Method 2</u>

We compute the <u>difference</u> in amount between x_{n+1} and x_n

(i.e. $\Delta x_n = x_{n+1} - x_n$). Hence we compute the losses an gains from year n

to year $n + 1$.

<u>Loss:</u> -10 service charge

<u>Gain:</u>   5% on amount after service charge (i.e. $+ 0.05(x_n - 10)$)

Net difference: $\Delta x_n = -10 + 0.05(x_n - 10)$

or $x_{n+1} - x_n = -10 + 0.05(x_n - 10)$

$\Rightarrow \quad x_{n+1} = (x_n - 10) + 0.05(x_n - 10)$

$\Rightarrow \quad x_{n+1} = 1.05(x_n - 10)$

$\Rightarrow \quad x_{n+1} = 1.05x_n - 10.5$

(b) Recall that if $x_{n+1} = ax_n + b$ then $x_n = \dfrac{b}{1-a} + \left(x_0 - \dfrac{b}{1-a}\right)a^n.$

In our case $a = 1.05$ and $b = -10.5$. Therefore

$$x_n = \frac{(-10.5)}{1 - 1.05} + \left(1000 - \frac{(-10.5)}{1 - 1.05}\right)(1.05)^n$$

$$x_n = 210 + 790(1.05)^n$$

which is the balance at the end of year n.

(c) The account will neither grow nor diminish if $x_0 - \dfrac{b}{1-a} = 0$ which will make

$\left(x_0 - \dfrac{b}{1-a}\right)a^n = 0$ and then $x_n = \dfrac{b}{1-a}$ for each year. Hence

$$x_0 - \frac{(-10.5)}{1 - 1.05} = 0 \quad \Rightarrow \quad x_0 = 210.$$

Hence the required initial deposit is \$210.

SOLUTIONS FOR LAB 7

PART B. Supplementary Problems

1. (i) $\displaystyle\lim_{x\to 0}\frac{\sqrt{x+16}-4}{x}=\lim_{x\to 0}\left(\frac{\sqrt{x+16}-4}{x}\right)\left(\frac{\sqrt{x+16}+4}{\sqrt{x+16}+4}\right)$

$\displaystyle =\lim_{x\to 0}\frac{\left(\sqrt{x+16}\right)^{2}-4^{2}}{x\left(\sqrt{x+16}+4\right)}=\lim_{x\to 0}\frac{x+16-16}{x\left(\sqrt{x+16}+4\right)}$

$\displaystyle =\lim_{x\to 0}\frac{x}{x\left(\sqrt{x+16}+4\right)}=\lim_{x\to 0}\frac{1}{\sqrt{x+16}+4}=\frac{1}{\sqrt{0+16}+4}=\frac{1}{8}$

(ii) $\displaystyle\lim_{x\to 4}\frac{x^{2}-11x+28}{x-4}=\lim_{x\to 4}\frac{(x-4)(x-7)}{(x-4)}=\lim_{x\to 4}(x-7)=4-7=-3$

(iii) $\displaystyle\lim_{x\to 0}\frac{\sqrt[3]{x+1}-1}{x}=\lim_{x\to 0}\left(\frac{(x+1)^{1/3}-1}{x}\right)\left(\frac{(x+1)^{2/3}+(x+1)^{1/3}+1}{(x+1)^{2/3}+(x+1)^{1/3}+1}\right)$

$\displaystyle =\lim_{x\to 0}\frac{\left((x+1)^{1/3}\right)^{3}-1^{3}}{x\left((x+1)^{2/3}+(x+1)^{1/3}+1\right)}$

$\displaystyle =\lim_{x\to 0}\frac{x+1-1}{x\left((x+1)^{2/3}+(x+1)^{1/3}+1\right)}$

$\displaystyle =\lim_{x\to 0}\frac{1}{(x+1)^{2/3}+(x+1)^{1/3}+1}=\frac{1}{(0+1)^{2/3}+(0+1)^{1/3}+1}=\frac{1}{3}$

(iv) $\displaystyle\lim_{x\to -2}\frac{x^{2}-x-6}{x^{2}+3x+2}=\lim_{x\to -2}\frac{(x-3)(x+2)}{(x+2)(x+1)}=\lim_{x\to -2}\frac{x-3}{x+1}$

$\displaystyle =\frac{-2-3}{-2+1}=\frac{-5}{-1}=5$

2. (a)

(i) $\lim\limits_{x \to 1^-} f(x) = \lim\limits_{x \to 1^-} [\![x]\!] = 0$

     $(x < 1)$ (see graph)

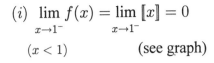

(ii) $\lim\limits_{x \to 1^+} f(x) = \lim\limits_{x \to 1^+} 1 = 1$

     $(1 < x < 2)$

(iii) $\lim\limits_{x \to 1} f(x)$ does not exist

     since $\lim\limits_{x \to 1^-} f(x) \neq \lim\limits_{x \to 1^+} f(x)$

(iv) $\lim\limits_{\substack{x \to 2^- \\ (1 < x < 2)}} f(x) = \lim\limits_{x \to 2^-} 1 = 1$

(v) $\lim\limits_{\substack{x \to 2^+ \\ (x > 2)}} f(x) = \lim\limits_{x \to 2^+} (x^2 - 3) = 1$

(vi) $\lim\limits_{x \to 2} f(x) = 1$ since $\lim\limits_{x \to 2^-} f(x) = \lim\limits_{x \to 2^+} f(x) = 1.$

A Note about the graph and the use of graphing software programs.

Notice that the part of the graph that represents the parabola $x^2 - 3$ appears to be a straight line instead of the curved parabola shape that you are expecting. For teaching purposes, if this graph were drawn freehand, the instructor would probably put a bit of a curve in that part of the graph to emphasis the fact that it represents a parabola. However graphing software programs are plotting exact values and depending on the scale you are using or which part of the parabola you are graphing, the graph you obtain, as in this case, could appear to be a straight line as demonstrated in the graph below.

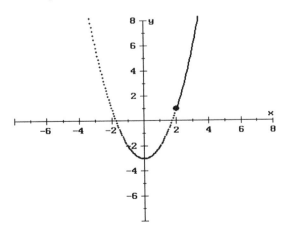

(b) f is <u>NOT</u> continuous at $x = -1$ because $\lim\limits_{x \to -1^-} f(x) = -2$ and

$\lim\limits_{x \to -1^+} f(x) = -1$ (see the graph) and since they are not equal, the $\lim\limits_{x \to -1} f(x)$

does not exist.

(c) f is continuous at $x = \dfrac{1}{2}$ because $\lim\limits_{x \to \frac{1}{2}} f(x) = f(\dfrac{1}{2}) = [\![\dfrac{1}{2}]\!] = 0$.

(d) f is <u>NOT</u> continuous at $x = 1$ since from (a) (i), (ii), and (iii) $\lim\limits_{x \to 1} f(x)$

does not exist.

(e) f is continuous at $x = 2$ since $f(2) = 1$, $\lim\limits_{x \to 2} f(x) = 1$ and hence

$\lim\limits_{x \to 2} f(x) = f(2) = 1$.

SOLUTIONS FOR LAB 8

PART B. Supplementary Problems

1. Recall that the average rate of change of f over $[a, b]$ is $\dfrac{f(b) - f(a)}{b - a}$. In this case we want the average rate of change of the function P over the interval $[2, 8]$. Hence

$$\frac{P(8) - P(2)}{8 - 2} = \frac{50 + \dfrac{100(8)}{20 + 8^2} - \left(50 + \dfrac{100(2)}{20 + 2^2}\right)}{8 - 2}$$

$$= \frac{\dfrac{100(8)}{84} - \dfrac{100(2)}{24}}{6} = 0.2 \,\text{mg/hr}.$$

2. We are given that $f(x) = 2\sin(\frac{\pi}{2}x)$ and $(x_0, f(x_0)) = (2, f(2)) = (2, 2\sin(\frac{\pi}{2}))$
$= (2, 0)$ and $(x_0 + \Delta x, f(x_0 + \Delta x)) = (3, f(3)) = (3, 2\sin(\frac{\pi}{2}(3))) = (3, -2)$.

The slope of the secant line is

$$m = \frac{f(x_0 + \Delta x) - f(x_0)}{\Delta x} = \frac{f(3) - f(2)}{1} = \frac{-2 - 0}{1} = -2.$$

Use the point $(2, f(2)) = (2, 0)$ and slope $m = -2$ to obtain
$$y - 0 = -2(x - 2) \implies y = -2x + 4$$
which is the equation of the secant line.

LAB 9
Solutions to Termtest II

Total Marks 20 $\begin{cases} \text{12 marks for the multiple choice questions} \\ \text{8 marks for the word problems} \end{cases}$

Each question in this part has exactly one correct answer. Circle your choice.

1. Which of the following arithmetic sequences has constant difference $d = 6$ and the 42nd term $a_{42} = 248$.

    (A) $\{10, 14, 18,...\}$

    (B) $\{4, 10, 16,...\}$

    (C) $\{2, 8, 14,...\}$

    (D) $\{6, 10, 14,...\}$

    (E) $\{3, 9, 15,...\}$

$$a_n = a_1 + (n-1)d \qquad d = 6$$
$$a_{42} = a_1 + 41(6) = 248$$
$$\Rightarrow a_1 = 248 - 246 = 2$$
$$\therefore \{2, 8, 14, \cdots\}$$

2. Which of the following is FALSE?

    (A) $\sum\limits_{i=0}^{60} i = 1830$

    (B) $\sum\limits_{i=1}^{25} 5(\tfrac{1}{3})^i = \tfrac{15}{2}\left(1 - (\tfrac{1}{3})^{25}\right)$

    (C) $\sum\limits_{i=1}^{10} i^3 = \tfrac{100(121)}{4}$

    (D) $\sum\limits_{k=8}^{24} (3^{k+1} - 3^k) = 3^{25} - 3^8$

    (E) $\sum\limits_{i=5}^{21} 2 = 34$

$$\sum_{i=1}^{N} g r^{i-1} = g\frac{(1-r^N)}{1-r}$$

$$\sum_{i=1}^{25} 5\left(\tfrac{1}{3}\right)^i = \sum_{i=1}^{25} 5\left(\tfrac{1}{3}\right)\left(\tfrac{1}{3}\right)^{i-1}$$

$$= \frac{5}{3}\frac{\left(1-(\tfrac{1}{3})^{25}\right)}{1-\tfrac{1}{3}}$$

$$= \left(\tfrac{5}{3}\right)\left(\tfrac{3}{2}\right)\left(1-\left(\tfrac{1}{3}\right)^{25}\right)$$

$$= \frac{5}{2}\left(1-\left(\tfrac{1}{3}\right)^{25}\right)$$

3. $\sum_{n=1}^{60} (10n - 4)$ equals

$10 \sum_{n=1}^{60} n - \sum_{n=1}^{60} 4$

(A) 17,400

(B) 17,700

$= \dfrac{10\,(60)(61)}{2} - 60(4)$

(C) 18,000

$= 18300 - 240$

(D) 18,060

$= 18\,060$

(E) 18,300

4. If a solution to $\triangle X_n = aX_n + b$ is $X_n = 540 - 300(\frac{2}{3})^n$ then the constant a equals

$X_{n+1} - X_n = a X_n + b$

(A) $\dfrac{1}{3}$

$\Rightarrow X_{n+1} = X_n + a X_n + b = (1+a) X_n + b$

(B) $-\dfrac{1}{3}$

Hence $1+a = \dfrac{2}{3} \Rightarrow a = -\dfrac{1}{3}$

(C) $-\dfrac{2}{3}$

(D) $\dfrac{2}{3}$

(E) 1

5. The positive equilibrium for the difference equation $X_{n+1} = - X_n (X_n - 4) + 10$ is

For equilibrium X_E

(A) 1

$X_E = - X_E (X_E - 4) + 10 = - X_E^2 + 4 X_E + 10$

(B) 2

$\Rightarrow X_E^2 - 3 X_E - 10 = 0$

(C) 4

$\Rightarrow (X_E - 5)(X_E + 2) = 0$

(D) 5

$\Rightarrow X_E = 5 \quad (positive)$

(E) 10

6. If $X_{n+1} = aX_n + 500$ where $0 < a < 1$ and the steady state $\overline{X} = \lim\limits_{n \to +\infty} X_n = 800$

then the constant a equals

(A) $\frac{1}{4}$

(B) $\frac{3}{8}$

(C) $\frac{1}{2}$

(D) $\frac{5}{8}$

(E) $\frac{7}{8}$

Since $0 < a < 1$ and $b = 500$

then $\overline{X} = \lim\limits_{n \to +\infty} X_n = \frac{b}{1-a} = 800$

$\Rightarrow \quad \frac{500}{1-a} = 800 \quad \Rightarrow \quad 1-a = \frac{500}{800}$

$\Rightarrow \quad 1-a = \frac{5}{8} \quad \Rightarrow \quad a = \frac{3}{8}$

7. $\lim\limits_{x \to 7} \dfrac{\sqrt{35+2x}-7}{x-7}$ equals

(A) $+\infty$

(B) $\frac{1}{14}$

(C) $\frac{1}{7}$

(D) $-\frac{1}{7}$

(E) $-\frac{1}{14}$

$\lim\limits_{x \to 7} \left(\dfrac{\sqrt{35+2x}-7}{x-7} \right) \left(\dfrac{\sqrt{35+2x}+7}{\sqrt{35+2x}+7} \right)$

$= \lim\limits_{x \to 7} \dfrac{(\sqrt{35+2x})^2 - 7^2}{(x-7)(\sqrt{35+2x}+7)}$

$= \lim\limits_{x \to 7} \dfrac{2x-14}{(x-7)(\sqrt{35+2x}+7)}$

$= \lim\limits_{x \to 7} \dfrac{2}{\sqrt{35+2x}+7} = \dfrac{2}{14} = \dfrac{1}{7}$

8. If $f(x) = \dfrac{1}{x-3}$ then the difference quotient $\dfrac{\triangle f(x)}{\triangle x} = \dfrac{f(x+h) - f(x)}{h}$, $h \neq 0$ equals

(A) $\dfrac{-1}{(x-3)(x+h-3)}$

(B) $\dfrac{1}{(x-3)(x+h-3)}$

(C) $\dfrac{-1}{(x-3)^2+h}$

(D) $\dfrac{-1}{x^2-9+h}$

(E) $\dfrac{-1}{(x+h-3)^2}$

$$\frac{\triangle f(x)}{\triangle x} = \frac{\frac{1}{(x+h)-3} - \frac{1}{x-3}}{h}$$

$$= \frac{\frac{x-3 - ((x+h)-3)}{(x-3)((x+h)-3)}}{h}$$

$$= \frac{-h}{h(x-3)(x+h-3)}$$

$$= \frac{-1}{(x-3)(x+h-3)}$$

9. Let B(t) denote the biomass (in mg) of a bacteria culture at time (in hours). If the average rate of change of the biomass B(t) from t=3 to t=10 hours is $\dfrac{5}{21}$ mg/hour and B(3) = 9 then B(10) equals

(A) $10\frac{2}{3}$ mg
(B) $9\frac{5}{7}$ mg
(C) $9\frac{2}{3}$ mg
(D) $8\frac{2}{3}$ mg
(E) $8\frac{5}{7}$ mg

$$\frac{B(10) - B(3)}{10-3} = \frac{5}{21}$$

$$\Rightarrow \frac{B(10) - 9}{7} = \frac{5}{21}$$

$$\Rightarrow B(10) = \frac{5}{3} + 9 = \frac{32}{3} = 10\frac{2}{3}$$

10. The slope of the tangent line to the graph of $f(t) = 2\,t^{-\frac{4}{3}}$ at the point (1, f(1)) is

(A) $-\dfrac{5}{8}$
(B) $-\dfrac{5}{2}$
(C) $-\dfrac{6}{5}$
(D) $\dfrac{7}{5}$
(E) $-\dfrac{8}{5}$

$$m = f'(t) = 2\left(-\frac{4}{5}\right)t^{-\frac{9}{5}}$$

$$\text{at } (1, f(1)) \quad m = f'(1) = \frac{-8}{5}(1)^{-\frac{9}{5}}$$

$$= -\frac{8}{5}$$

11. If y = sec(x) then y″ equals

(A) $\sec^3(x)\tan(x)$

(B) $\sec^3(x) + \sec^2(x)\tan(x)$

(C) $\sec^3(x) + \sec(x)\tan^2(x)$

(D) $\sec(x)\tan(x) + \sec^2(x)$

(E) $2\sec^2(x)\tan^2(x)$

$$y' = \sec(x)\tan(x)$$
$$y'' = \sec(x)(\sec^2(x)) + (\sec(x)\tan(x))\tan(x)$$
$$= \sec^3(x) + \sec(x)\tan^2(x)$$

12. If $f(x) = c\,x^{\frac{3}{2}} - 2x + 7$ where c is a constant and if the second derivative

f″(25) = 9 then c equals

(A) $\frac{27}{20}$

(B) $\frac{12}{5}$

(C) $\frac{14}{15}$

(D) 60

(E) 12

$$f'(x) = \frac{3}{2}\,Cx^{\frac{1}{2}} - 2$$
$$f''(x) = \frac{3}{4}\,Cx^{-\frac{1}{2}}$$
$$f''(25) = \frac{3}{4}\,C(25)^{-\frac{1}{2}} = 9$$
$$\Rightarrow C = \frac{9(5)(4)}{3} = 60$$

PART II

Work each problem. Show all your work in the space provided.

13. Let $f(x) = \begin{cases} 5\sin(4x) + 6 & \text{if } x < 0 \\ 6e^{-\frac{x}{3}} & \text{if } 0 \le x < 6 \\ 2\ln(x-5) & \text{if } x \ge 6 \end{cases}$

(A) Compute the following:

(i) $\lim\limits_{x \to 0^-} f(x) = \lim\limits_{\substack{x \to 0^- \\ (x<0)}} 5\sin(4x) + 6 = 6$

(ii) $\lim\limits_{x \to 0^+} f(x) = \lim\limits_{\substack{x \to 0^+ \\ (0<x<6)}} 6e^{-\frac{x}{3}} = 6e^0 = 6$

②

(iii) $\lim\limits_{x \to 6^-} f(x) = \lim\limits_{\substack{x \to 6^- \\ (0<x<6)}} 6e^{-\frac{x}{3}} = 6e^{-2}$

(iv) $\lim\limits_{x \to 6^+} f(x) = \lim\limits_{\substack{x \to 6^+ \\ (x>6)}} 2\ln(x-5) = 2\ln(1) = 0$

(B) Is f continuous at $x = 0$? Explain your answer.

Yes since $\lim\limits_{x \to 0^-} f(x) = \lim\limits_{x \to 0^+} f(x) = \lim\limits_{x \to 0} f(x) = 6$

and $f(0) = 6e^0 = 6$

14. Suppose that the size in milligrams of a cell culture is given by $M(t) = t + \dfrac{25}{t^2}$ for $t > 0.1$, where t is measured in hours.

(A) At what rate is the size of the cell culture changing at t = 5 hours?

$$M(t) = t + 25t^{-2} \implies m'(t) = 1 \cdot 50 t^{-3}$$

$$\implies m'(t) = 1 - \frac{50}{t^3}$$

$$m'(5) = 1 - \frac{50}{5^3} = 1 - \frac{50}{125} = 1 - \frac{2}{5} = \frac{3}{5}$$

Increasing at a rate of $\frac{3}{5}$ mg/hr.

①

(B) At what time will the growth rate of the culture be zero?

Find t when $m'(t) = 0$

$$\implies 1 - \frac{50}{t^3} = 0$$

$$\implies t^3 = 50 \implies t = (50)^{\frac{1}{3}}$$

in $t = (50)^{\frac{1}{3}} \approx 3.68$ hrs.

①

15. In an insecticide testing experiment on a controlled population of insects it was observed that each month, before the spraying, 400 insects were removed and the remaining insect population decreased by 10% as a result of the spraying. After the decrease, 500 insects were added to the population. Let X_n denote the size of the population at month n.

(A) State the difference equation representing the change in size of the population each month.

$$\Delta X_n = -400 - 0.1\left(X_n - 400\right) + 500$$

$$\Rightarrow X_{n+1} - X_n = -400 - 0.1 X_n + 40 + 500$$

$$X_{n+1} = 0.9 X_n + 140$$

(1)

(B) If the initial population was 5,000 then find the size of the insect population at the end of the nth month.

$$X_{n+1} = a X_n + b \qquad a = 0.9 \quad b = 140 \quad X_0 = 5000$$

$$X_n = \frac{b}{1-a} + \left(X_0 - \frac{b}{1-a}\right)a^n$$

$$X_n = \frac{140}{1-.9} + \left(5000 - \frac{140}{1-.9}\right)(.9)^n$$

$$X_n = 1400 + 3600\,(0.9)^n$$

(1)

16. A certain difference equation modelled by $X_{n+1} = f(X_n)$ corresponds to the following graph:

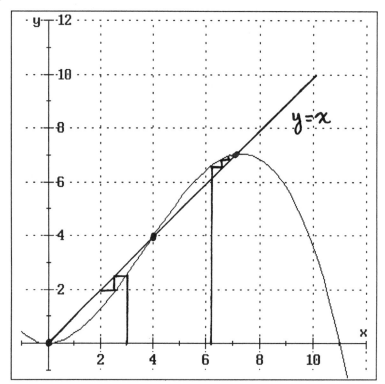

(A) Estimate the equilibriums of the system.

$$0, 4, 7$$

(B) If $X_5 = 3$ then estimate X_7.

$$X_7 \approx 2$$

(C) Is the largest equilibrium value stable or unstable? Illustrate on the diagram.

STABLE

SOLUTIONS FOR LAB 10

PART B. Supplementary Problems

  1. (a) $f(x) = 3x^4 - 8x^3$ (b) $f(x) = x^{5/3} - 5x^{2/3}$

      $f'(x) = 12x^3 - 24x^2$ $f'(x) = \frac{5}{3}x^{\frac{2}{3}} - \frac{10}{3}x^{-\frac{1}{3}}$

      $\Rightarrow f'(x) = 12x^2(x-2)$ $\Rightarrow f'(x) = \frac{5x-10}{3x^{1/3}}$

      $f''(x) = 36x^2 - 48x$ $f''(x) = \frac{10}{9}x^{-\frac{1}{3}} + \frac{10}{9}x^{-\frac{4}{3}}$

    (i) <u>Critical Points</u>: $x = 0,\ x = 2$ $x = 0,\ x = 2$

   (ii) <u>Local Extrema</u>:   local min. at $x = 2$ local max. at $x = 0$

                                                        local min. at $x = 2$

  (iii) <u>f increasing on</u>: $(2, +\infty)$ $(-\infty, 0) \cup (2, +\infty)$

      <u>f decreasing on</u>: $(-\infty, 2)$ $(0, 2)$

   (iv) <u>Concave Up</u>: $(-\infty, 0) \cup \left(\frac{4}{3}, +\infty\right)$ $(-1, +\infty)$

       <u>Concave Down</u>: $\left(0, \frac{4}{3}\right)$ $(-\infty, -1)$

    (v) <u>Points of Inflection</u>: $(0,0),\ \left(\frac{4}{3}, -9\frac{13}{27}\right)$ $(-1, -6)$

   (vi) x-intercepts $x^3(3x - 8) = 0$ $x^{\frac{2}{3}}(x - 1) = 0$

                             $x = 0,\ x = \frac{8}{3}$ $x = 0,\ x = 1$

Labeling for the Graph:

$$A = (0,0) \quad B = \left(\frac{4}{3},\ -9\frac{13}{27}\right) \qquad\qquad A = (-1, -6) \quad B = (0, 0)$$

$$C = (2, -16) \quad D = \left(\frac{8}{3}, 0\right) \qquad\qquad C = (2, -3(2^{\frac{2}{3}})) \approx (2, -4.76)$$

$$D = (5, 0)$$

Graph of $f(x) = 3x^4 - 8x^3$　　　　　Graph $f(x) = x^{5/3} - 5x^{2/3}$

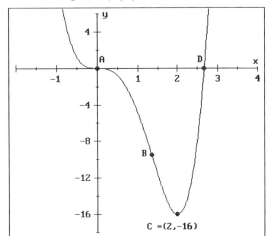

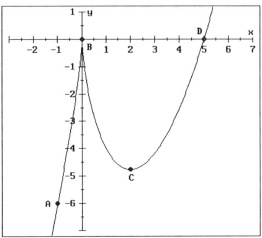

A Note About the Graph and the Use of graphing software programs.

In the graph of $f(x) = x^{5/3} - 5x^{2/3}$, notice the shape of the graph about the point of inflection $A = (-1, -6)$ and the point $B = (0, 0)$. The change in concavity is not noticeable about the point of inflection $(-1, -6)$ and the graph does not appear to reach the point $(0, 0)$. Be careful what conclusions you arrive at when you view the software-generated graph. In this case, if you knew nothing about this function, based on the graph, you would have concluded that there were no points of inflections. The concavity change about the point of inflection was slight and the scaling that was used made the graph appear to be a straight line through the point of inflection. The graph appeared not to reach (0, 0) but if fact does.

2.　　Let $n \geq 30$ denote the number of trees per acre and let $A(n)$ denote the total yield of peaches per acre with n planted trees.

The average yield per tree for $n \geq 30$ is　　　　　$600 - 10(n - 30)$

and the total yield per acre for these n trees is

$$A(n) = n(600 - 10(n - 30)) \quad \Rightarrow \quad A(n) = n(900 - 10n) = 900n - 10n^2$$

Find the critical points by setting $A'(n) = 0$.

$$A'(n) = 900 - 20n = 0 \quad \Rightarrow \quad n = 45.$$

Since $A''(n) = -20$ and $A''(45) = -20 < 0$ there is a local max. at $n = 45$.

Since $A(n)$ is a quadratic function then there is a global max. at $n = 45$. Hence there should be 45 trees per acre to maximize the total peach yield.

3. Given $C(t) = \frac{A}{r-s}(e^{-st} - e^{-rt})$ $A, r, s > 0, \quad r > s$

$\quad\quad C'(t) = \frac{A}{r-s}(-se^{-st} + re^{-rt}) = 0$

Since $\frac{A}{r-s} \neq 0 \;\Rightarrow\; -se^{-st} + re^{-rt} = 0$

$\quad\quad\quad\quad\quad\quad\quad \Leftrightarrow\; re^{-rt} = se^{-st}$

$\quad\quad\quad\quad\quad\quad\quad \Leftrightarrow\; r = se^{rt-st}$

$\quad\quad\quad\quad\quad\quad\quad \Leftrightarrow\; e^{(r-s)t} = \frac{r}{s}$

(take ln) $\quad\quad\quad\quad \Leftrightarrow\; (r-s)t = \ln\left(\frac{r}{s}\right)$

$\quad\quad\quad\quad\quad\quad\quad \Leftrightarrow\; t = \frac{1}{r-s}\ln\left(\frac{r}{s}\right)$ <u>Critical Point</u>

We use the 2nd derivative test to check to see if a maximum occurs at
$t = \frac{1}{r-s}\ln\left(\frac{r}{s}\right)$.

$A''(t) = \frac{A}{r-s}(s^2 e^{-st} - r^2 e^{-rt}) = \frac{A}{r-s}e^{-rt}(s^2 e^{rt-st} - r^2)$

<u>NOTE:</u> $\frac{A}{r-s}e^{-rt} > 0$ for all t hence the only part of $A''(t)$ that can change its

sign is the factor $(s^2 e^{(r-s)t} - r^2)$.

We substitute $t = \frac{1}{r-s}\ln\left(\frac{r}{s}\right)$ in this part to obtain

$s^2 e^{(r-s)\left(\frac{1}{r-s}\right)\ln(r/s)} - r^2 = s^2 e^{\ln(r/s)} - r^2 = s^2\left(\frac{r}{s}\right) - r^2 = sr - r^2$

Since $s < r$ and $r > 0$ then $sr < r^2$ and hence

$$sr\text{-}r^2 < 0 \qquad\qquad (1)$$

From above $\qquad \dfrac{A}{r-s}e^{-rt} > 0$ for all t $\qquad (2)$

Hence (1) and (2) yield that $A''\left(\dfrac{1}{r-s}\ln\left(\dfrac{r}{s}\right)\right) < 0$.

Hence there is a maximum at $t = \dfrac{1}{r-s}\ln\left(\dfrac{r}{s}\right)$.

SOLUTIONS FOR LAB 11

PART B. Supplementary Problems

1. (i) Volume of sphere $V = \dfrac{4}{3}\pi r^3$, $r_0 = 4$, $dr = -0.05$.

   Approximate change in the volume

   $$dV = 4\pi r^2\, dr$$

   $$\Rightarrow\ dV = 4\pi(4)^2(-0.05) = -3.2\pi\ \text{m}^3$$

   (ii) Surface Area of the sphere $S = 4\pi r^2$.

   Approximate change in the surface area

   $$dS = 8\pi r\, dr$$

   $$\Rightarrow\ dS = 8\pi(4)(-0.05) = -1.6\pi\ \text{m}^2$$

   (iii) Approximate relative change in the volume.

   $$\frac{dV}{V} = \frac{4\pi r^2\, dr}{(4/3)\pi r^3} = 3\frac{dr}{r} = \frac{3(-0.05)}{4} = -0.0375$$

   Approximate relative change in the surface area.

   $$\frac{dS}{S} = \frac{8\pi r\, dr}{4\pi r^2} = 2\frac{dr}{r} = \frac{2(-0.05)}{4} = -0.025$$

2. Surface Area of the sphere is $S = 4\pi r^2$. We are given that $r_0 = 3$ and $dr = \pm 0.03$.

   Approximate error in the surface area:

   $$dS = 8\pi r\, dr = 8\pi(3)(\pm 0.03) = \pm 0.72\pi\ \text{cm}^2$$

   Percentage Error:

   $$100\left(\frac{dS}{S}\right) = 100\left(\frac{8\pi r\, dr}{4\pi r^2}\right) = 100\left(\frac{2\, dr}{r}\right) = \frac{100(2)(0.03)}{3} = 2\%$$

3. We are given that $100\left(\dfrac{dr}{r}\right) = 0.1$ and we are required to find $100\left(\dfrac{dV}{V}\right)$. Hence

$$100\left(\frac{dV}{V}\right) = 100\left(\frac{4\pi r^2\,dr}{(4/3)\pi r^3}\right) = 100\left(\frac{3\,dr}{r}\right) = 3\left(100\left(\frac{dr}{r}\right)\right)$$

$$= 3(0.1) = 0.3\ .$$

Hence the maximum percentage error in the volume is 0.3%.

4. We are given $x^2 + y^2 = e^{xy}$ and (1,0). We differentiate the equation implicitly with respect to x to obtain y' and then we substitute $(1,0)$ to obtain the slope of the required tangent line.

$$2x + 2y\,y' = e^{xy}\,D_x(xy)$$

$$\Rightarrow\ 2x + 2y\,y' = e^{xy}\,(y + xy')$$

$$\Rightarrow\ 2x + 2y\,y' = y\,e^{xy} + xy'\,e^{xy}$$

(Solve for y')
$$\Rightarrow\ (2y - x\,e^{xy})\,y' = y\,e^{xy} - 2x$$

$$\Rightarrow\ y' = \frac{y\,e^{xy} - 2x}{2y - x\,e^{xy}}$$

(Slope of tangent line)
$$\Rightarrow\ y'\Big|_{\substack{x=1\\y=0}} = \frac{0\,e^0 - 2(1)}{2(0) - 1\,e^0} = \frac{-2}{-1} = 2$$

Equation of the tangent line is

$$y - 0 = 2(x - 1)\ \Rightarrow\ y = 2x - 2$$

5. Recall that the 3rd order Taylor Polynomial approximation of f about x_0 is

$$f(x) \approx f(x_0) + f'(x_0)\,(x - x_0) + \frac{f''(x_0)}{2!}(x - x_0)^2 + \frac{f'''(x_0)}{3!}(x - x_0)^3.$$

In our question $f(x) = \ln(x)$ and $x_0 = 1$

$$f(x) = \ln(x) \qquad f(1) = \ln(1) = 0$$

$$f'(x) = \frac{1}{x} \qquad f'(1) = \frac{1}{1} = 1$$

$$f''(x) = -\frac{1}{x^2} \qquad f''(1) = -\frac{1}{1^2} = -1$$

$$f'''(x) = \frac{2}{x^3} \qquad f'''(1) = \frac{2}{1^3} = 2$$

Hence

$$f(x) = \ln(x) \approx 0 + 1\,(x-1) + \frac{(-1)}{2!}(x-1)^2 + \frac{(2)}{3!}(x-1)^3$$

$$\ln(x) \approx (x-1) - \frac{1}{2}(x-1)^2 + \frac{1}{3}(x-1)^3.$$

6.   Recall that the 4th order Taylor polynomial approximation of the function f about $x = x_0$ is

$$f(x) \approx f(x_0) + f'(x_0)\,(x-x_0) + \frac{f''(x_0)}{2!}(x-x_0)^2 + \frac{f'''(x_0)}{3!}(x-x_0)^3 + \frac{f^{(4)}(x_0)}{4!}(x-x_0)^4$$

For $f(x) = \sin(x)$ and $x_0 = 1.5\pi = \frac{3\pi}{2}$:

$$f(x) = \sin(x) \qquad \sin(\tfrac{3\pi}{2}) = -1$$

$$f'(x) = \cos(x) \qquad \cos(\tfrac{3\pi}{2}) = 0$$

$$f''(x) = -\sin(x) \qquad -\sin(\tfrac{3\pi}{2}) = 1$$

$$f'''(x) = -\cos(x) \qquad -\cos(\tfrac{3\pi}{2}) = 0$$

$$f^{(4)}(x) = \sin(x) \qquad \sin(\tfrac{3\pi}{2}) = -1$$

and hence

$$\sin(x) \approx -1 + \frac{1}{2}(x - \tfrac{3\pi}{2})^2 - \frac{1}{24}(x - \tfrac{3\pi}{2})^4$$

For $x = 1.5\pi + 0.01$

$$\sin(1.5\pi + 0.01) \approx -1 + \frac{1}{2}(.01)^2 - \frac{1}{24}(.01)^4$$

$$\approx -.9999500004 .$$

7.   Let $f(x) = \sqrt{x} = x^{\frac{1}{2}}$, $x_0 = 4$. The third order Taylor polynomial of f about x_0 is

$$f(x) \approx f(x_0) + f'(x_0)(x - x_0) + \frac{f''(x_0)}{2!}(x - x_0)^2 + \frac{f'''(x_0)}{3!}(x - x_0)^3 .$$

For $f(x) = x^{\frac{1}{2}}$ and $x_0 = 4$:

$f(x) = x^{\frac{1}{2}}$ $f(4) = 4^{\frac{1}{2}} = 2$

$f'(x) = \frac{1}{2} x^{-\frac{1}{2}}$ $f'(4) = \frac{1}{2(4)^{\frac{1}{2}}} = \frac{1}{4}$

$f''(x) = -\frac{1}{4} x^{-\frac{3}{2}}$ $f''(4) = -\frac{1}{4(4)^{\frac{3}{2}}} = -\frac{1}{32}$

$f'''(x) = \frac{3}{8} x^{-\frac{5}{2}}$ $f'''(4) = \frac{3}{8(4)^{\frac{5}{2}}} = \frac{3}{256}$

and hence

$$f(x) \approx 2 + \frac{1}{4}(x - 4) - \frac{\frac{1}{32}}{2!}(x - 4)^2 + \frac{\frac{3}{256}}{3!}(x - 4)^3$$

$\Rightarrow$ $f(x) \approx 2 + \frac{1}{4}(x - 4) - \frac{1}{64}(x - 4)^2 + \frac{1}{512}(x - 4)^3 .$

For x = 4.24

$$f(4.24) = \sqrt{4.24} \approx 2 + \frac{1}{4}(.24) - \frac{1}{64}(.24)^2 + \frac{1}{512}(.24)^3$$

$\Rightarrow$ $\sqrt{4.24} \approx 2.059127.$

SOLUTIONS FOR LAB 12

PART B. Supplementary Problems

1.   (i) $P(t) = \int r(t)\, dt = \int (3t^2 + t)\, dt$

    (ii) $P(t) = \int (3t^2 + t)\, dt = t^3 + \dfrac{t^2}{2} + C$

        We are given that $P(0) = 100$ which yields that

$$P(0) = 100 = 0^3 + \frac{0^2}{2} + C \quad \Rightarrow \quad C = 100\ .$$

        Hence $P(t) = t^3 + \dfrac{t^2}{2} + 100$ and

$$P(2) = 2^3 + \frac{2^2}{2} + 100 = 110.$$

2.   Since $f(t) = 3e^t$ is the rate of change of the number of revolutions per minute then

    (i) $RPM(t) = \int f(t)\, dt = \int 3e^t\, dt = 3e^t + C\ .$

   We are given that $RPM(0) = 0$ which yields that

$$0 = 3e^0 + C \quad \Rightarrow \quad 0 = 3 + C \quad \Rightarrow \quad C = -3.$$

   Hence $RPM(t) = 3e^t - 3$ and for $t = T$

$$RPM(T) = 3e^T - 3$$

   and for $T = 5$

$$RPM(5) = 3e^5 - 3 \ \text{rev./min.}\ .$$

Course Review

Solutions to Final Exam

Total Marks 44 $\begin{cases} \textbf{26 marks for the multiple choice questions} \\ \textbf{18 marks for the word problems} \end{cases}$

PART I

Each question in this part has exactly one correct answer. Remember to **CIRCLE** your answer on this questionnaire and clearly indicate your answer on the computer score sheet.

1. If $f(x) = e^{3x+4} - 2$, the inverse function f^{-1} is given by

   (a) $f^{-1}(x) = \frac{1}{e^{3x+4} - 2}$

   (b) $f^{-1}(x) = \frac{1}{3} ln(x+2) + \frac{4}{3}$

   (c) $f^{-1}(x) = \frac{1}{3} ln(x+2) - \frac{4}{3}$

   (d) $f^{-1}(x) = \frac{1}{3} ln(x+4) - \frac{2}{3}$

   (e) $f^{-1}(x) = \frac{1}{3} ln(x+4) + \frac{2}{3}$

   $Let \; y = e^{3x+4} - 2$
   $\Rightarrow e^{3x+4} = y + 2$
   $\Rightarrow 3x + 4 = ln(y+2)$
   $\Rightarrow x = \frac{1}{3}(ln(y+2) - 4)$
   $\therefore f^{-1}(x) = \frac{1}{3} ln(x+2) - \frac{4}{3}$

2. If $\{a_n\}$ is an arithmetic sequence with $a_1 = 8$ and $a_{11} = 68$ then a_{31} is

   (a) 120

   (b) 168

   (c) 188

   (d) 198

   (e) 208

   $a_n = a_1 + (n-1)d = 8 + (n-1)d$
   $a_{11} = 68 = 8 + 10d \Rightarrow 10d = 60 \Rightarrow d = 6$
   $\therefore a_{31} = 8 + 30(6) = 188$

3. An equation that passes through (8, 200) and whose graph on log-log paper is a straight line with slope $\frac{2}{3}$ is

Must have form $y = cx^k$ with $k = \frac{2}{3}$

(a) $y = 200\, x^{\frac{2}{3}}$

Possible (a) or (d)

(b) $y = 200\, (2)^{x-8}$

Sub. $x = 8$ in (a) $y = 200(8)^{\frac{2}{3}} = 800$

(c) $y = 200\, (2)^{\frac{2x}{3}}$ "   "   " (d) $y = 50(8)^{\frac{2}{3}} = 200$

(d) $y = 50\, x^{\frac{2}{3}}$ ⟵ circled

(e) $y = \frac{2}{3}\, x + \frac{584}{3}$

4. Let $f(x) = \begin{cases} ln(2x^2 + 1) & \text{if } x \leq 0 \\ \sin(\llbracket x \rrbracket) & \text{if } 0 < x < 1 \\ 3^{x-1} & \text{if } x \geq 1 \end{cases}$,

where $\llbracket x \rrbracket$ is the greatest integer of x. Which of the following is false?

(a) $\lim\limits_{x \to \frac{\pi}{4}} f(x) = 0$

(b) $\lim\limits_{x \to 0^+} f(x) = 0$

$\lim\limits_{x \to 1^+} f(x) = \lim\limits_{x \to 1^+} 3^{x-1} = 3^{1-1} = 3^0 = 1 \neq 0$

(c) $\lim\limits_{x \to 0^-} f(x) = 0$ $(x > 1)$

(d) $\lim\limits_{x \to 1^+} f(x) = 0$ ⟵ circled

(e) $\lim\limits_{x \to 1^-} f(x) = 0$

5. If $\triangle X_n = -\frac{1}{5}X_n + 300$ and $X_0 = 2500$ then X_n equals

   (a) $1300(-\frac{3}{5})^n + 700$

   (b) $1000(\frac{2}{5})^n + 1500$

   (c) $2000(\frac{4}{5})^n + 500$

   (d) $1750(\frac{4}{5})^n + 750$

   (e) $1000(\frac{4}{5})^n + 1500$

   $X_{n+1} - X_n = -\frac{1}{5}X_n + 300$

   $\Rightarrow X_{n+1} = \frac{4}{5}X_n + 300$

   $a = \frac{4}{5} \quad b = 300$

   $X_n = \frac{b}{1-a} + \left(X_0 - \frac{b}{1-a}\right)a^n$

   $= \frac{300}{1-\frac{4}{5}} + \left(2500 - \frac{300}{1-\frac{4}{5}}\right)\left(\frac{4}{5}\right)^n$

   $= 1500 + 1000\left(\frac{4}{5}\right)^n$

6. The equilibrium for the equation $\triangle X_n = -\frac{1}{3}X_n - 2$ is

   (a) 6

   (b) 3

   (c) $\frac{3}{2}$

   (d) $-\frac{3}{2}$

   (e) -6

   $\Rightarrow X_{n+1} - X_n = -\frac{1}{3}X_n - 2$

   $X_{n+1} = \frac{2}{3}X_n - 2$

   For X_E: $X_E = \frac{2}{3}X_E - 2$

   $\Rightarrow \frac{1}{3}X_E = -2$

   $\Rightarrow X_E = -6$

7. A function with basic period 10 and a maximum value of 70 is

   (a) $30\sin(\frac{\pi x}{5}) + 40$

   (b) $70\sin(10x)$

   (c) $70\sin(\frac{\pi x}{10})$

   (d) $70\sin(\frac{\pi x}{5}) + 70$

   (e) $40\sin(\frac{x}{5}) + 30$

   $\sin(ax)$ with $B.P. = \frac{2\pi}{a} = 10 \Rightarrow a = \frac{\pi}{5}$

   $\therefore (a) \text{ or } (d)$

   when $\sin(\frac{\pi}{5}x) = 1 \quad (a) \Rightarrow 30 + 40 = 70$

   (max of sine)

8. If $2\left(\log_b(16) - \log_b(2)\right) + 3 = 9$ then b is

    (a) 2

    (b) e

    (c) 3

    (d) 4

    (e) 10

$$\log_b(16) - \log_b(2) = \frac{9-3}{2} = 3$$
$$\Longleftarrow \log_b\left(\frac{16}{2}\right) = \log_b(8) = 3$$
$$\Longleftarrow 8 = b^3 \Longleftrightarrow b = 2$$

9. The population of a bacterial culture at time t, in hours, is given by $P(t) = 2^t$. The average rate of change of the population over the interval $[3, 7]$ is

    (a) 28 bacteria/hr

    (b) 30 bacteria/hr

    (c) 32 bacteria/hr

    (d) 34 bacteria/hr

    (e) 36 bacteria/hr

$$\frac{P(b) - P(a)}{b-a} = \frac{P(7) - P(3)}{7-3} = \frac{2^7 - 2^3}{4}$$
$$= \frac{2^2(2^5 - 2)}{4} = 30$$

10. If the size of the nth generation of a population of fruit flies is given by $P_n = 100 + \sum_{t=1}^{n}(t - 20)$, then which of the following is the size of the 200th generation?

    (a) 16000

    (b) 16100

    (c) 16200

    (d) 16300

    (e) 16400

$$P_{200} = 100 + \sum_{t=1}^{200}(t-20) = 100 + \sum_{t=1}^{200}t - \sum_{t=1}^{200}20$$
$$= 100 + \frac{200(201)}{2} - 200(20)$$
$$= 100 + 20100 - 4000 = 16200$$

11. Which of the following functions has a graph that is the same as the graph of $y = ln(2x)$, but shifted right 3 units and upwards 2 units?

(a) $y = 2 + ln(2x+3)$

(b) $y = 2 + ln(2(x+3))$

(c) $y = 2 + ln(2(x - 3))$

(d) $y = 2 + ln(2x - 3)$

(e) $y = 3 + ln(2(x+2))$

$$f(x) = ln(2x)$$
$$y = f(x-3) + 2$$
$$= ln(2(x-3)) + 2$$

12. Assume that the growth rate of a chicken, $R(t)$, is a quadratic function of the number of days t since the chicken was hatched. Assume that the chicken is not growing at hatching and ceases to grow after 80 days. If the chicken's maximum growth rate is $R_{max} = 10$, then the equation for $R(t)$ is:

(a) $R(t) = -\frac{1}{160}(t - 40)^2 + 10$

(b) $R(t) = \frac{1}{160}(t - 40)^2 + 10$

(c) $R(t) = -\frac{1}{160}(t + 40)^2 + 10$

(d) $R(t) = -\frac{1}{40}(t - 40)^2 + 10$

(e) $R(t) = -\frac{1}{160}(t - 80)^2 + 10$

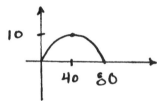

$$R(t) = c(t - b)^2 + a$$

From graph: $b = 40$, $a = 10$
and $c < 0$

$$R(t) = c(t - 40)^2 + 10$$
$$R(0) = c(0 - 40)^2 + 10 = 0$$
$$1600c = -10$$
$$c = -\frac{1}{160}$$
$$R(t) = -\frac{1}{160}(t - 40)^2 + 10$$

13. Which one of the following is **FALSE?**

   (a) The $(n + 1)$ th derivative of a polynomial of degree n is zero.

   (b) A function $f(x)$ is continuous at $x = a$ if $\lim_{x \to a} f(x) = f(a)$.

   (c) A function is increasing on (a, b) if x_1, x_2 in (a, b) and $x_1 < x_2$ implies that $f(x_1) > f(x_2)$. $f(x_1) < f(x_2)$

   (d) The definite integral of a continuous function $f(x)$ over $[a, b]$ is given by $\int_a^b f(x)\, dx = F(b) - F(a)$ where $F(x)$ is an antiderivative of $f(x)$.

   (e) $\int_a^b k\, f(x)\, dx = k \int_a^b f(x)\, dx$ where k is a constant.

14. The population size $P(t)$ of a bacteria culture at time t (in hours) was given, by $P(t) = k(2+t)^3$ where k is a constant. If the rate of growth at $t = 2$ hours was 9600 bacteria/hour then the value of k is

   (a) 50
   (b) 100
   (c) 150
   (d) 200
   (e) 250

$$P'(t) = 3k(2+t)^2$$
$$P'(2) = 9600 = 3k(2+2)^2 \Rightarrow 9600 = 48\,k$$
$$\Rightarrow k = \frac{9600}{48} = 200$$

15. The distance s from a fixed point to a bead moving on a straight wire is related to the time t by $s(t) = t^2\sin(t)$. The acceleration $A(t)$ at time t is given by

   (a) $2\sin(t) + 4t\cos(t) + t^2\sin(t)$

   (b) $2\sin(t) - 4t\cos(t) - t^2\sin(t)$

   (c) $2t^2\sin(t) + 4t\cos(t)$

   (d) $2t\sin(t) + t^2\cos(t)$

   (e) $2\sin(t) + 4t\cos(t) - t^2\sin(t)$

$$V(t) = s'(t) = 2t\sin(t) + t^2\cos(t)$$
$$A(t) = s''(t) = 2\sin(t) + 2t\cos(t)$$
$$+ 2t\cos(t) - t^2\sin(t)$$
$$= 2\sin(t) + 4t\cos(t) - t^2\sin(t)$$

16. $\displaystyle\lim_{x \to 9} \left(\frac{\frac{1}{x-6} - \frac{1}{3}}{x - 9} \right)$ equals $\displaystyle\lim_{x \to 9} \frac{\frac{3-(x-6)}{3(x-6)}}{x-9} = \lim_{x\to 9} \frac{(9-x)^{-1}}{3(x-6)(x-9)}$

$= \displaystyle\lim_{x\to 9} \frac{-1}{3(x-6)} = -\frac{1}{9}$

   (a) $+\infty$

   (b) $\frac{1}{9}$

   (c) 0

   (d) $-\frac{1}{9}$

   (e) $-\infty$

17. $D_x \left(e^{\cos^2(\sqrt{x})} \right)$ equals $e^{\cos^2(x^{1/2})} D_x \cos^2(x^{\frac{1}{2}})$

$= e^{\cos^2(x^{1/2})} (-2)\cos(x^{1/2})\sin(x^{1/2})(\frac{1}{2})x^{-\frac{1}{2}}$

$= -\frac{1}{\sqrt{x}} e^{\cos^2(\sqrt{x})} \cos(\sqrt{x})\sin(\sqrt{x})$

   (a) $\frac{2}{\sqrt{x}} \cos(\sqrt{x})\sin(\sqrt{x}) e^{\cos^2(\sqrt{x})}$

   (b) $-\frac{2}{\sqrt{x}} \cos(\sqrt{x})\sin(\sqrt{x}) e^{\cos^2(\sqrt{x})}$

   (c) $\frac{1}{\sqrt{x}} \cos(\sqrt{x})\sin(\sqrt{x}) e^{\cos^2(\sqrt{x})}$

   (d) $-\frac{1}{\sqrt{x}} \cos(\sqrt{x})\sin(\sqrt{x}) e^{\cos^2(\sqrt{x})}$

   (e) $\cos^2(\sqrt{x}) e^{\cos^2(\sqrt{x})-1}$

18. If $x^2 + e^{xy} + y = 2x$ then y' equals

$2x + e^{xy}(xy'+y) + y' = 2$

$xe^{xy}y' + y' = 2-2x-ye^{xy}$

$y'(xe^{xy}+1) = 2-2x-ye^{xy}$

$y' = \frac{2-2x-ye^{xy}}{xe^{xy}+1}$

   (a) $\frac{2-2x}{xe^{xy}+1}$

   (b) $\frac{2-2x-ye^{xy}}{xe^{xy}}$

   (c) $\frac{2-2x-xe^{xy}}{xe^{xy}}$

   (d) $\frac{2-2x-ye^{xy}}{xe^{xy}+1}$

   (e) $\frac{2-2x-xe^{xy}}{ye^{xy}}$

19. $\int x \sqrt{5 - x^2} \, dx$ equals

    (a) $\frac{1}{3}(5 - x^2)^{\frac{3}{2}} + C$

    (b) $-\frac{1}{3}(5 - x^2)^{\frac{3}{2}} + C$

    (c) $\frac{2}{3}(5 - x^2)^{\frac{3}{2}} + C$

    (d) $-\frac{2}{3}(5 - x^2)^{\frac{3}{2}} + C$

    (e) $\frac{2}{3}x(5 - x^2)^{\frac{3}{2}} + C$

Handwritten:

Let $u = 5 - x^2 \Rightarrow u' = -2x$

$\Rightarrow x = -\dfrac{u'}{2}$

$\therefore \int x\sqrt{5-x^2}\,dx = -\dfrac{1}{2}\int u^{\frac{1}{2}} u' \, dx$

$= \left(-\dfrac{1}{2}\right)\dfrac{u^{3/2}}{\frac{3}{2}} + C = -\dfrac{1}{3}(5-x^2)^{\frac{3}{2}} + C$

(b) circled

20. Which of the following is **false?**

    (a) The definite integral of f(x) over [a, b] is defined by

$$\int_a^b f(x)\,dx = \lim_{\substack{N \to +\infty \\ \triangle x \to 0}} \sum_{n=1}^{N} f(x_n^*)\,\triangle x_n.$$

    (b) An antiderivative of a function f(x) is a function F(x) such that $F'(x) = f(x)$.

    (c) The differential of $y = f(x)$ is defined by $dy = f'(x)dx$

    (d) The natural domain of the function $y = e^{-2x}$ is $(-\infty, +\infty)$.

    (e) The function $y = \ln(x-2)$ is decreasing for all x in $(2, +\infty)$.

(e) circled; "decreasing" underlined with "increasing" written below

21. $\int_4^{16} \dfrac{dx}{\sqrt{x}}$ is equal to

    (a) 2

    (b) 4

    (c) 6

    (d) 8

    (e) 12

Handwritten:

$\int x^{-\frac{1}{2}}dx = 2x^{\frac{1}{2}} + C$

$\therefore \int_4^{16} \dfrac{dx}{\sqrt{x}} = 2x^{\frac{1}{2}}\Big|_4^{16} = 2(16)^{\frac{1}{2}} - 2(4)^{\frac{1}{2}}$

$= 8 - 4 = 4$

(b) circled

22. If $y = x^{(x^3)}$ then y' is equal to

(a) $x^2 + 3x^2 \, ln(x)$

(b) $x^3 x^{x^3 - 1}$

(c) $x^{(x^3)} \left(x^2 + 3x^2 \, ln(x) \right)$

(d) $3x^2 \left(x^{x^3 - 1} \right)$

(e) $x^{(x^3)} \, x^3 \, ln(x)$

$$y = x^{x^3}$$

$$\Rightarrow ln(y) = ln\left(x^{x^3}\right) = x^3 \, ln(x)$$

Diff. w.r.t. x

$$\Rightarrow \frac{1}{y} y' = 3x^2 \, ln(x) + x^3 \left(\frac{1}{x}\right)$$

$$\Rightarrow y' = y\left(3x^2 \, ln(x) + x^2\right)$$

$$\Rightarrow y' = x^{x^3}\left(3x^2 \, ln(x) + x^2\right)$$

23. $\int_0^{\pi} \cos(x) \sin^3(x) \, dx$ equals

(a) -1

(b) $-\frac{1}{4}$

(c) 0

(d) $\frac{1}{4}$

(e) 1

Let $u = \sin(x)$, $u' = \cos(x)$

$$\int \cos(x) \sin^3(x) \, dx = \int u^3 u' \, dx = \frac{u^4}{4} + C = \frac{\sin^4(x)}{4} + C$$

$$\therefore \int_0^{\pi} \cos(x) \sin^3(x) \, dx = \left. \frac{\sin^4(x)}{4} \right|_0^{\pi} = \frac{\sin^4(\pi)}{4} - \frac{\sin^4(0)}{4}$$

$$= 0 - 0 = 0$$

24. If 2,400 g of a radioactive material decays exponentially with decay rate $k = \frac{1}{200}$ then the number of grams of this material that is left by the time $t = 200 ln(4)$ years is

(a) $\frac{2}{3}$

(b) 300

(c) 600

(d) 900

(e) $1,500$

$$A(t) = A_0 e^{-kt} = 2400 e^{-\frac{1}{200}t}$$

$$A(200 \, ln(4)) = 2400 e^{-\frac{1}{200}(200 \, ln(4))}$$

$$= 2400 e^{-ln(4)}$$

$$= 2400 \frac{1}{e^{ln(4)}}$$

$$= \frac{2400}{4} = 600$$

25. If the size of a cell culture at time t is given by the function $F(t) = te^{-\frac{1}{5}t}$
    for t ≥ 0, then the size of the culture is a maximum when t equals

    (a) 0

    (b) $\frac{1}{3}$

    (c) $\frac{1}{5}$

    (d) 3

    (e) 5

$$F'(t) = e^{-\frac{1}{5}t} + t\left(-\frac{1}{5}\right)e^{-\frac{1}{5}t}$$

$$= e^{-\frac{1}{5}t}\left(1 - \frac{1}{5}t\right) = 0$$

$$\Rightarrow t = 5$$

$$F''(t) = -\frac{1}{5}e^{-\frac{1}{5}t}\left(1 - \frac{1}{5}t\right) - \frac{1}{5}e^{-\frac{1}{5}t}$$

$$F''(5) < 0$$

26. The third order Taylor polynomial approximation about $x_0 = 3$ of the

    function $f(x) = e^{2x-6}$ is

    (a) $1 + 2(x - 3) + 4(x - 3)^2 + 8(x - 3)^3$

    (b) $1 + 2x + 4x^2 + 8x^3$

    (c) $1 + 2x + \frac{2}{3}x^2 + \frac{4}{3}x^3$

    (d) $1 + 2(x - 3) + 2(x - 3)^2 + \frac{4}{3}(x - 3)^3$

    (e) $1 + 2(x+3) + 2(x+3)^2 + \frac{4}{3}(x+3)^3$

$$f(x) \approx f(3) + f'(3)(x-3) + \frac{f''(3)}{2!}(x-3)^2$$
$$+ \frac{f'''(3)}{3!}(x-3)^3$$

$$f(x) = e^{2x-6} \qquad f(3) = e^{6-6} = e^0 = 1$$

$$f'(x) = 2e^{2x-6} \qquad f'(3) = 2e^0 = 2$$

$$f''(x) = 4e^{2x-6} \qquad f''(3) = 4e^0 = 4$$

$$f'''(x) = 8e^{2x-6} \qquad f'''(3) = 8e^0 = 8$$

$$\therefore f(x) \approx 1 + 2(x-3) + 2(x-3)^2 + \frac{4}{3}(x-3)^3$$

PART II

Work each problem. Show all your work in the space provided.

27. (a) Find the finite area bounded by the graphs of $f(x) = 3x$ and $g(x) = x^2 - x$. Sketch the area.

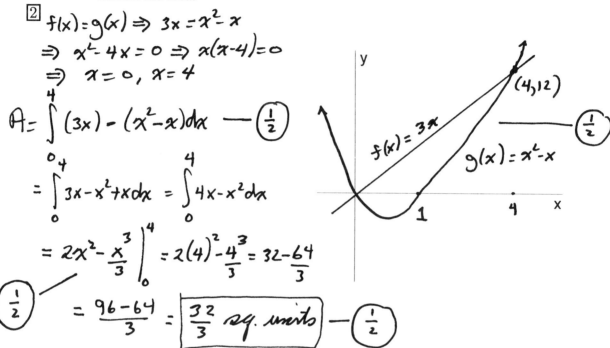

$$\boxed{2} \quad f(x) = g(x) \Rightarrow 3x = x^2 - x$$
$$\Rightarrow x^2 - 4x = 0 \Rightarrow x(x-4) = 0$$
$$\Rightarrow x = 0, \ x = 4$$

$$A = \int_0^4 (3x) - (x^2 - x)\, dx \quad - \textcircled{\tfrac{1}{2}}$$

$$= \int_0^4 3x - x^2 + x\, dx = \int_0^4 4x - x^2\, dx$$

$$= 2x^2 - \frac{x^3}{3}\Big|_0^4 = 2(4)^2 - \frac{4^3}{3} = 32 - \frac{64}{3}$$

$$\textcircled{\tfrac{1}{2}} \quad = \frac{96 - 64}{3} = \boxed{\frac{32}{3} \text{ sq. units}} - \textcircled{\tfrac{1}{2}}$$

(b) A healing wound is circular in shape. The radius was $r = 3$ cm and 24 hours later the radius was 2.8 cm. (The area of a circle is $A = \pi r^2$)

(i) Use differentials to approximate the decrease in the area of the wound in the 24 hour period.

$$\boxed{2} \quad dA = 2\pi r_0\, dr \qquad\qquad dr = -.2 \qquad r_0 = 3$$

$$= 2\pi(3)(-.2) \qquad\qquad \textcircled{1}$$

$$= -1.2\,\pi$$

Approximate decrease 1.2π cm^2

(ii) Find the approximate relative percentage change in the surface area of the wound in the 24 hour period.

$$100\left(\frac{dA}{A}\right) = 100\,\frac{2\pi r\, dr}{\pi r^2} = 200\,\frac{dr}{r} \qquad \textcircled{1}$$

$$= 200\left(\frac{-.2}{3}\right) = -\frac{40}{3}$$

Approximate relative % decrease is $\frac{40}{3}$%

28. (a) A biological variable y(t) = k sin(aπt + b) + c, where k, a, b and c are
constants, varies sinusoidally with period 80 days, attaining its minimum
at t = 40 days. If the maximum and minimum values are 95 and 35
respectively, determine the constants k, a, b and c.

Basic Period : $80 = \dfrac{2\pi}{a\pi} \Rightarrow a = \dfrac{2}{80} = \dfrac{1}{40}$

2 Amplitude : $k = \dfrac{max-min}{2} = \dfrac{95-35}{2} = 30$

$\therefore \quad y = 30 \sin\left(\dfrac{\pi}{40}t\right) \Rightarrow$

From graph :

$\qquad y = 30 \sin\left(\dfrac{\pi}{40}(t+20)\right)$

shift 20 units
For min at t = 40

$C = $ upward shift $= \dfrac{max+min}{2} = \dfrac{95+35}{2} = 65$

Model : $\quad y = 30 \sin\left(\dfrac{\pi}{40}(t+20)\right) + 65$

$\qquad\qquad = 30 \sin\left(\dfrac{\pi}{40}t + \dfrac{\pi}{2}\right) + 65$

$\therefore \quad \boxed{k = 30} \quad \boxed{a = \dfrac{1}{40}} \quad \boxed{b = \dfrac{\pi}{2}} \quad \boxed{c = 65}$

$\left(\dfrac{1}{2}\right)$ each

(b) **Approximate** the definite integral $\int_0^8 xe^x\, dx$ by using a uniform
partition of size N = 4 and the right end point of each subinterval for
evaluation (Do not attempt to evaluate the exponentials).

2 $h = \dfrac{b-a}{N} = \dfrac{8-0}{4} = 2 \quad \therefore P = \{0, 2, 4, 6, 8\}$

Evaluation Pts: $x_1^* = 2, \ x_2^* = 4, \ x_3^* = 6, \ x_4^* = 8$

$f(x) = xe^x$

$\therefore \int_0^8 f(x)\, dx \approx f(2)(2) + f(4)(2) + f(6)(2) + f(8)(2)$

$\qquad\qquad \approx 2\left[2e^2 + 4e^4 + 6e^6 + 8e^8\right]$

29. For the function $f(x) = 4x^3 - 12x^2 + 16$

(a) Find all local extrema for $y = f(x)$.

$f'(x) = 12x^2 - 24x = 12x(x-2) = 0$

$\Rightarrow x = 0, \ x = 2$

$f''(x) = 24x - 24 = 24(x-1)$

$f''(0) = -24 < 0 \quad local\ max$

$f''(2) = 24 > 0 \quad local\ min$

Answer
local max at x=0
local min at x=2

(b) Indicate the intervals on which the graph of $y = f(x)$ is concave upward and concave downward.

□1 $f''(x) = 24(x-1) = 0 \Rightarrow x = 1$

concave upward
$(1, +\infty)$

concave downward
$(-\infty, 1)$

(c) Find the points of inflection

□1 Sign of f'' changes about $x = 1$ where

$f''(1) = 0$

$\therefore (1, f(1)) = (1, 8)$ pt. of inflection

Answer
$(1, 8)$

(d) Sketch the graph of y = f(x). Label the local extrema points and points of inflection.

2

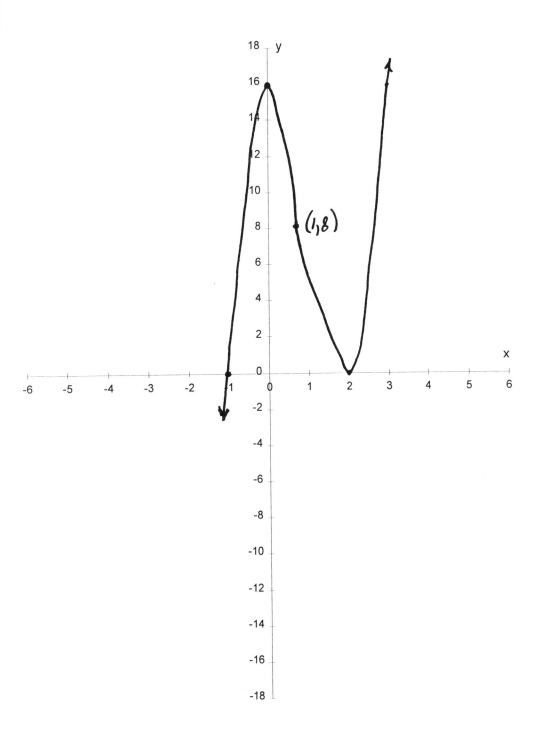

30. (a) A discrete dynamical system is given by the difference equation

$$X_{n+1} = f(X_n) \text{ where f is given by the graph}$$

③

(i) What are the equilibrums of this system?

0 and 6

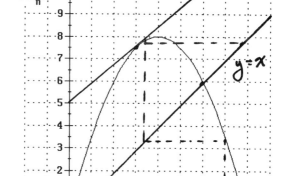

(ii) If $X_4 = 7$ estimate X_6.

$$X_6 \approx 7.6$$

(iii) Estimate the value X_0 for which the slope of the tangent line to the graph of f is one.

$$\boxed{X_0 = 3}$$

(b) Evaluate $\int_0^1 9x \sqrt{3x+1} \, dx$.   let $u = 3x+1 \Rightarrow x = \dfrac{u-1}{3}$

$$
\begin{array}{ll}
x=1 & u=4 \\
x=0 & u=1
\end{array}
\qquad
\begin{array}{l}
du = 3\, dx \\
3\, du = 9\, dx
\end{array}
$$

$$\int_0^1 9x\sqrt{3x+1}\, dx = \int_1^4 3\left(\frac{u-1}{3}\right) u^{1/2}\, du = \int_1^4 u^{3/2} - u^{1/2}\, du$$

②
$$= \frac{2}{5} u^{5/2} - \frac{2}{3} u^{3/2} \Big|_1^4 = \frac{2}{5}(4)^{5/2} - \frac{2}{3}(4)^{3/2} - \frac{2}{5} + \frac{2}{3}$$

$$= \frac{2}{5}(32) - \frac{2}{3}(8) - \frac{2}{5} + \frac{2}{3} = \frac{62}{5} - \frac{14}{3} = \frac{186-70}{15} = \frac{116}{15}$$

A
   P
      P
         E
            N
               D
                  I
                     X

Supplementary Differentiation Problems

Find f'.

1. $f(x) = \sin(3x)$

2. $f(x) = x^{5/3} + 2x^{4/3} - 3x^{-1/3}$

3. $f(x) = \sqrt[3]{(x^3 + 3x + 2)^2}$

4. $f(x) = \dfrac{x}{\ln(x)}$

5. $f(x) = (2x + 3)^4 (3x - 2)^{7/3}$

6. $f(x) = \dfrac{\sqrt[3]{2 + 6x}}{x}$

7. $f(s) = \dfrac{\sqrt{s^2 + 1}}{s}$

8. $f(t) = (\cos(t))(t^5 - 4t)$

9. $f(x) = \dfrac{x^3 + 2}{\sin(x)}$

10. $f(w) = \dfrac{3}{4} w^{4/3} + 2w^{1/2} - 2w^{-1}$

11. $f(y) = \dfrac{2y + 3}{\sqrt{y^2 + 3y + 4}}$

12. $f(x) = \sin^3(x)$

13. $f(x) = \sin^3(x^2 + 1)$

14. $f(x) = e^{(x^2 + 2)}$

15. $f(x) = 3^{x^2}$

16. $f(x) = \tan(\pi x)$

17. $f(x) = \cot(\pi x^2 + 2x)$

18. $f(x) = \ln(x^2)$

19. $f(x) = \ln(x^3 + 3x + 2)$

20. $g(x) = \sqrt{\tan(x)}$

21. $f(x) = \dfrac{x \cos(x)}{\ln(x)}$

22. $f(x) = \cos^2(\tan(x))$

23. $f(x) = \cos^2(\tan(x^2 + 1))$

24. $f(x) = x \ln(x)$

25. $f(x) = \ln(x) \cos^2(x)$

26. $f(x) = \ln(x^2) \cos^2(x)$

27. $f(x) = \dfrac{\ln(x^2)}{\cos^2(x)}$

28. $f(r) = \dfrac{\sqrt{1 + 4r^2}}{r^2}$

29. $f(x) = \sqrt{\dfrac{3x-2}{2x+3}}$

30. $f(t) = t^2 \left(\dfrac{3t+4}{3t-2}\right)^{1/3}$

31. $f(x) = \dfrac{x^2 \sin(x) + 1}{e^x}$

32. $f(x) = \dfrac{\sin(x)}{x^2 + 1}$

33. $f(x) = \dfrac{\sin(x^2)}{x^2 + 1}$

34. $f(x) = \dfrac{\cos(x)}{\ln(x^2)}$

35. $f(x) = 3^{\cot(x^2)}$

36. $f(x) = x^3 \tan(x^2)[\sec^2(x) - \cot(x^2)]$

37. $f(x) = e^{x^2} \tan(x)$

38. $f(x) = e^{e^{x^2}}$

Answers to Supplementary Differentiation Problems

1. $3\cos(3x)$

2. $\dfrac{5}{3}x^{2/3} + \dfrac{8}{3}x^{1/3} + x^{-4/3}$

3. $2(x^2 + 1)(x^3 + 3x + 2)^{-1/3}$

4. $\dfrac{\ln(x) - 1}{\ln^2(x)}$

5. $7(2x+3)^4(3x-2)^{4/3} + 8(2x+3)^3(3x-2)^{7/3} = (2x+3)^3(3x-2)^{4/3}(38x+5)$

6. $\dfrac{2x(2+6x)^{-2/3} - (2+6x)^{1/3}}{x^2} = \dfrac{-2(1+2x)}{x^2(2+6x)^{2/3}}$

7. $\dfrac{s^2(s^2+1)^{-1/2} - (s^2+1)^{1/2}}{s^2} = \dfrac{-1}{s^2(s^2+1)^{1/2}}$

8. $(\cos(t))(5t^4 - 4) - (\sin(t))(t^5 - 4t)$

9. $\dfrac{3x^2 \sin(x) - (x^3 + 2)\cos(x)}{\sin^2(x)}$

10. $w^{1/3} + w^{-1/2} + 2w^{-2}$

11. $\dfrac{4(y^2 + 3y + 4)^{1/2} - (2y+3)^2(y^2+3y+4)^{-1/2}}{2(y^2+3y+4)}$

12. $3\sin^2(x)\cos(x)$

13. $6x\sin^2(x^2+1)\cos(x^2+1)$

14. $2x\,e^{x^2} + 2$

15. $2x\ln(3)\,3^{x^2}$

16. $\pi\sec^2(\pi x)$

17. $-(2\pi x + 2)\csc^2(\pi x^2 + 2x)$

18. $\dfrac{2}{x}$

19. $\dfrac{3x^2 + 3}{x^3 + 3x + 2}$

20. $\dfrac{1}{2}(\tan(x))^{-1/2}\sec^2(x)$

21. $\dfrac{\ln(x)[\cos(x) - x\sin(x)] - \cos(x)}{\ln^2(x)}$

22. $-2\sec^2(x)\cos(\tan(x))\sin(\tan(x))$

23. $-4\sec^2(x^2+1)\cos(\tan(x^2+1))\sin(\tan(x^2+1))$

24. $1+\ln(x)$

25. $-2\ln(x)\cos(x)\sin(x)+\dfrac{1}{x}\cos^2(x)=-\ln(x)\sin(2x)+\dfrac{1}{x}\cos^2(x)$

26. $-2\cos(x)\sin(x)\ln(x^2)+\dfrac{2}{x}\cos^2(x)=-\sin(2x)\ln(x^2)+\dfrac{2}{x}\cos^2(x)$

27. $\dfrac{\dfrac{2}{x}\cos^2(x)+2\sin(x)\cos(x)\ln(x^2)}{\cos^4(x)}=\dfrac{2\cos^2(x)+x\sin(2x)\ln(x^2)}{x\cos^4(x)}$

28. $\dfrac{4r^3\left(1+4r^2\right)^{-1/2}-2r\left(1+4r^2\right)^{1/2}}{r^4}=\dfrac{-2(1+2r^2)}{r^3\left(1+4r^2\right)^{1/2}}$

29. $\dfrac{1}{2}\left(\dfrac{3x-2}{2x+3}\right)^{-1/2}\left(\dfrac{13}{(2x+3)^2}\right)=\dfrac{13}{2(3x-2)^{1/2}(2x+3)^{3/2}}$

30. $-6t^2\left(\dfrac{3t+4}{3t-2}\right)^{-2/3}\left(\dfrac{1}{3t-2}\right)^2+2t\left(\dfrac{3t+4}{3t-2}\right)^{1/3}=\dfrac{2t(9t^2+3t-8)}{(3t+4)^{2/3}(3t-2)^{4/3}}$

31. $\dfrac{x^2\cos(x)+2x\sin(x)-x^2\sin(x)-1}{e^x}$

32. $\dfrac{(x^2+1)\cos(x)-2x\sin(x)}{(x^2+1)^2}$

33. $\dfrac{(x^2+1)2x\cos(x^2)-2x\sin(x^2)}{(x^2+1)^2}$

34. $\dfrac{-x\ln(x^2)\sin(x)-2\cos(x)}{x(\ln(x^2))^2}$

35. $-2x\ln(3)\csc^2(x^2)\,3^{\cot(x^2)}$

36. $2[x^3+\tan(x^2)][\sec^2(x)\tan(x)+x\csc^2(x^2)]$

   $+[3x^2-2x\sec^2(x^2)][\sec^2(x)-\cot(x^2)]$

37. $e^{x^2}\sec^2(x)+2x\,e^{x^2}\tan(x)$

38. $2x\,e^{x^2}e^{e^{x^2}}$

Supplementary Integration Problems

Find the integral.

1. $\int \left(3e^t - 5t^3 + 7 + \dfrac{3}{t} \right) dt$

2. $\int 3^{2t} \, dt$

3. $\int 2 \sin(2x) \, dx$

4. $\int e^{3x} \, dx$

5. $\int \cos(3x) \, dx$

6. $\int 1 \, dx$

7. $\int 2 \, dx$

8. $\int \dfrac{\ln(6x)}{x} \, dx$

9. $\int \tan^2(x) \, dx$ (Hint: use a trig formula)

10. $\int \dfrac{1 + 3x + 7x^2 - 2x^3}{x^2} \, dx$

11. $\int \sin^6(t) \cos(t) \, dt$

12. $\int e^{2x} \cos(e^{2x}) \, dx$

13. $\int \dfrac{\ln^2(x)}{x} \, dx$

14. $\int \dfrac{\ln^2(x^2)}{x} \, dx$

15. $\int \left(3\theta^2 - 6\theta + \dfrac{9}{\theta} + 4\,e^\theta \right) d\theta$

16. $\int \dfrac{(t - t^2)^2}{t\sqrt{t}} \, dt$

17. $\int \dfrac{\cos(x)}{\sin(x)} \, dx$

18. $\int \tan(x) \, dx$ (Hint: see question 17)

19. $\int \dfrac{y}{\sqrt{1 + y^2}} \, dy$

20. $\int 2x \, 5^{x^2} \, dx$

21. $\int \dfrac{1}{x \ln^2(x)} \, dx$

22. $\int \dfrac{\cos(x)}{(1 + \sin(x))^2} \, dx$

23. $\int x \, 3^{x^2} \sin(3^{x^2}) \, dx$

24. $\int \dfrac{1}{x \ln(x)} \, dx$

25. $\int \dfrac{\sec^2(x)}{1 + \tan(x)} \, dx$

26. $\int \dfrac{1}{x} \sin(\ln(x)) \, dx$

27. $\int \dfrac{2x^5 + 3x^4 + x^3 + 7x^2 + 9x + 3}{x^3 + 3}\, dx$

28. $\int \cos(3x + 11)\, dx$

29. $\int x^4 \sin(x^5 + 7)\, dx$

30. $\int 8 \sin(x) \cos(x)\, dx$

31. $\int t^2\, e^{(t^3 + 1)}\, dt$

32. $\int \csc^5(6x) \cot(6x)\, dx$

Answers to Supplementary Integration Problems

1. $3\,e^t - \dfrac{5}{4}t^4 + 7t + 3\ln(t) + C$

2. $\dfrac{3^{2t}}{2\ln(3)} + C$

3. $-\cos(2x) + C$

4. $\dfrac{1}{3}e^{3x} + C$

5. $\dfrac{1}{3}\sin(3x) + C$

6. $x + C$

7. $2x + C$

8. $\dfrac{1}{2}\ln^2(6x) + C$

9. $-x + \tan(x) + C$

10. $-x^2 + 7x + 3\ln(x) - \dfrac{1}{x} + C$

11. $\dfrac{1}{7}\sin^7(t) + C$

12. $\dfrac{1}{2}\sin(e^{2x}) + C$

13. $\dfrac{1}{3}\ln^3(x) + C$

14. $\dfrac{1}{6}\ln^3(x^2) + C$

15. $\theta^3 - 3\theta^2 + 9\ln(\theta) + 4\,e^{\theta} + C$

16. $\dfrac{2}{7}t^{7/2} - \dfrac{4}{5}t^{5/2} + \dfrac{2}{3}t^{3/2} + C$

17. $\ln(\sin(x)) + C$

18. $-\ln(\cos(x)) + C$

19. $(1 + y^2)^{1/2} + C$

20. $\dfrac{5^{x^2}}{\ln(5)} + C$

21. $\dfrac{-1}{\ln(x)} + C$

22. $\dfrac{-1}{1 + \sin(x)} + C$

23. $\left(\dfrac{-1}{2\ln(3)}\right)\cos(3^{x^2}) + C$

24. $\ln(\ln(x)) + C$

25. $\ln(1 + \tan(x)) + C$

26. $-\cos(\ln(x)) + C$

27. $\dfrac{2}{3}x^3 + \dfrac{3}{2}x^2 + x + \dfrac{1}{3}\ln(x^3 + 3) + C$

28. $\dfrac{1}{3}\sin(3x + 11) + C$

29. $-\dfrac{1}{5}\cos(x^5 + 7) + C$

30. $4\sin^2(x) + C$ or $-4\cos^2(x) + C$

31. $\dfrac{1}{3}e^{t^3 + 1} + C$

32. $-\dfrac{1}{30}\csc^5(6x) + C$

$\boxed{\textit{OVERHEADS}}$

DERIVATIVE FORMULAE

1. $D_x C = 0$ C a constant

2. $D_x x^r = r\, x^{r-1}$ r real

3. $D_x \sin(x) = \cos(x)$

4. $D_x \cos(x) = -\sin(x)$

5. $D_x \tan(x) = \sec^2(x)$

6. $D_x \csc(x) = -\csc(x)\cot(x)$

7. $D_x \sec(x) = \sec(x)\tan(x)$

8. $D_x \cot(x) = -\csc^2(x)$

9. $D_x e^x = e^x$

10. $D_x \ln(x) = \dfrac{1}{x}$

11. $D_x b^x = \ln(b)\, b^x$

12. $D_x \log_b(x) = \dfrac{1}{\ln(b)}\, \dfrac{1}{x}$

CHAIN RULE

LET u BE A DIFFERENTIABLE FUNCTION OF x.

1. $D_x u^r = r\, u^{r-1} u'$ or $D_x[f(x)]^r = r[f(x)]^{r-1}\, f'(x)$

2. $D_x \sin(u) = \cos(u)u'$

3. $D_x \cos(u) = -\sin(u)u'$

4. $D_x \tan(u) = \sec^2(u)u'$

5. $D_x \csc(u) = -\csc(u)\cot(u)u'$

6. $D_x \sec(u) = \sec(u)\tan(u)u'$

7. $D_x \cot(u) = -\csc^2(u)u'$

8. $D_x e^u = e^u\, u'$

9. $D_x \ln(u) = \dfrac{1}{u}\, u'$

10. $D_x b^u = \ln(b)\, b^u\, u'$

11. $D_x \log_b(u) = \dfrac{1}{\ln(b)}\, \dfrac{1}{u}\, u'$

DIFFERENTIATION

ALGEBRA OF FUNCTIONS

Let f and g be differentiable functions of x.

$$D_x (k\, f(x)) = kD_x f(x)$$

$$D_x (f(x) + g(x)) = D_x f(x) + D_x g(x)$$

$$D_x (f(x) - g(x)) = D_x f(x) - D_x g(x)$$

$$D_x (f(x)\, g(x)) = f(x)D_x g(x) + g(x)D_x f(x)$$

$$D_x \left(\frac{f(x)}{g(x)}\right) = \frac{g(x)D_x f(x) - f(x)D_x g(x)}{[g(x)]^2}$$

Integral Formulae

1. $\int x^r dx = \frac{x^{r+1}}{r+1} + C \quad$ r real, $r \neq -1$

2. $\int \cos(x)\, dx = \sin(x) + C$

3. $\int \sin(x)\, dx = -\cos(x) + C$

4. $\int \sec^2(x)\, dx = \tan(x) + C$

5. $\int \csc(x)\cot(x)\, dx = -\csc(x) + C$

6. $\int \sec(x)\tan(x)\, dx = \sec(x) + C$

7. $\int \csc^2(x)\, dx = -\cot(x) + C$

8. $\int e^x\, dx = e^x + C$

9. $\int \frac{1}{x}\, dx = \ln(x) + C \qquad x > 0$

10. $\int b^x\, dx = \frac{b^x}{\ln(b)} + C$

Integral Formulae

1. $\int u^r\, u'\, dx = \dfrac{u^{r+1}}{r+1} + C \quad$ r real, $r \neq -1$

2. $\int \cos(u) u'\, dx = \sin(u) + C$

3. $\int \sin(u) u'\, dx = -\cos(u) + C$

4. $\int \sec^2(u) u'\, dx = \tan(u) + C$

5. $\int \csc(u)\cot(u) u'\, dx = -\csc(u) + C$

6. $\int \sec(u)\tan(u) u'\, dx = \sec(u) + C$

7. $\int \csc^2(u) u'\, dx = -\cot(u) + C$

8. $\int e^u\, u'\, dx = e^u + C$

9. $\int \dfrac{1}{u}\, u'\, dx = \ln(u) + C \quad\quad u > 0$

10. $\int b^u\, u'\, dx = \dfrac{b^u}{\ln(b)} + C$

CURVE SKETCHING AND MAX. MIN. PROBLEMS

Increasing and Decreasing Functions

(i)   A function f is **increasing** on (a,b) if $x_1, x_2 \varepsilon$ (a,b) and $x_1 < x_2$ then
$f(x_1) < f(x_2)$

(ii) A function f is **decreasing** on (a,b) if $x_1, x_2 \varepsilon$ (a,b) and $x_1 < x_2$ then
$f(x_1) > f(x_2)$

USING DERIVATIVES

Assume f is a differentiable function of x

INCREASING AND DECREASING

At a Point x_0

(i) f is **increasing** at x_0 if $f'(x_0) > 0$

(ii) f is **decreasing** at x_0 if $f'(x_0) < 0$

(iii) f is **stationary** at x_0 if $f'(x_0) = 0$

ON AN INTERVAL (a, b)

(i) f is **increasing** on (a, b) if $f'(x) > 0$ for all $x \varepsilon$ (a, b)

(ii) f is **decreasing** on (a, b) if $f'(x) < 0$ for all $x \varepsilon$ (a, b)

CRITICAL POINTS

DEFINITION

Assume f is continuous on (a, b) and $x_0 \; \varepsilon$ (a, b)   (note this $\Rightarrow \; x_0 \; \varepsilon \; D_f$)

then x_0 is a ***CRITICAL POINT OF f*** if either

     (i) $\; f'(x_0) = 0$

or   (ii) $\; f'(x_0)$ DOES NOT EXIST.

EXAMPLES

1. Find the critical points and where the function is increasing and decreasing for

$$f(x) = \tfrac{1}{3}x^3 - \tfrac{1}{2}x^2 - 6x \; .$$

2. Find the critical points of
$$f(x) = \sqrt{x^2 - 1} \; .$$

LOCAL MAX. AND LOCAL MIN.

Definition

1. f has a **local maximum** at $x = x_0$ if $f(x) < f(x_0)$ for all x

   in some open interval about x_0 .

2. f has a **local minimum** at $x = x_0$ if $f(x) > f(x_0)$ for all x

   in some open interval about x_0 .

Definition

f has an **EXTREMUM** at x_0 if f has either a **local maximum**

or a **local minimum** at x_0 .

GLOBAL MAXIMUM AND GLOBAL MINIMUM

Definition

1. f has a **global maximum** M on a set S if there is $x_M \varepsilon$ S such that

$$f(x_M) = M \text{ and } f(x) \leq M \text{ for all } x \varepsilon S.$$

2. f has a **global minimum** m on a set S if there is $x_m \varepsilon$ S such that

$$f(x_m) = m \text{ and } f(x) \geq m \text{ for all } x \varepsilon S.$$

FIRST DERIVATIVE TEST

FOR DETERMINING

LOCAL MAX.'S OR LOCAL MIN.'S

Let x_0 be a critical point of f and let f'(x) be defined in an open interval containing x_0.

1.   f has a **local maximum** at x_0 if

    f'(x) $>$ **0** to the **immediate left** of x_0 and

    f'(x) $<$ **0** to the **immediate right** of x_0.

2.   f has a **local minimum** at x_0 if

    f'(x) $<$ **0** to the **immediate left** of x_0 and

    f'(x) $>$ **0** to the **immediate right** of x_0.

3.   If the **sign of f'(x) DOES NOT CHANGE ABOUT** x_0 then

    f has **neither a local max. nor a local min. at** x_0.

CONCAVITY OF THE GRAPH OF f

Definition

Let f be differentiable at $x = x_0$

1.   The graph of f is **concave downward** at $x = x_0$ if the graph of f is

   below the tangent line at $(x_0, f(x_0))$ in some open interval about x_0 .

2.   The graph of f is **concave upward** at $x = x_0$ if the graph of f is

   above the tangent line at $(x_0, f(x_0))$ in some open interval about x_0 .

USING THE SECOND DERIVATIVE f″
TO DETERMINE THE CONCAVITY OF A GRAPH

Assume that f is differentiable twice (i.e. f″ is defined) on an interval (a,b) containing x_0.

1. If $f''(x_0) > 0$, then the graph of f is **concave upward** at $x=x_0$

2. If $f''(x_0) < 0$, then the graph of f is **concave downward** at $x=x_0$.

HENCE

1.   If $f''(x) > 0$ for all $x \in$ (a,b) then the graph of f is **concave upward** over (a,b) .

2.   If $f''(x) < 0$ for all $x \in$ (a,b) then the graph of f is **concave downward** over (a,b) .

POINT OF INFLECTION

A point $(x_0, f(x_0))$ on the graph of f is a **point of inflection** if the graph changes concavity at x_0.

From above, we see that the change in concavity at x_0 will occur if the

sign of f″ changes about x_0 .

USING f″ TO FIND POSSIBLE POINTS OF INFLECTION

Assume f is defined on (a,b) and f′ and f″ are defined on (a,b) except possibly at $x_0 \varepsilon$ (a,b).

The point $(x_0, f(x_0))$ is a **possible point of inflection** on the graph of f if either

(i) $f''(x_0) = 0$ or

(ii) $f''(x_0)$ IS UNDEFINED.

ONCE YOU HAVE FOUND THE POSSIBLE POINT OF INFLECTION

$(x_0, f(x_0))$ YOU CHECK TO SEE IF THE SIGN OF f″ CHANGES ABOUT x_0. IF IT DOES YOU HAVE A POINT OF INFLECTION AND IF IT DOESN'T CHANGE THEN $(x_0, f(x_0))$ IS NOT A POINT OF INFLECTION.

THE SECOND DERIVATIVE TEST

FOR DETERMINING LOCAL EXTREMA

Assume that f is differentiable on (a,b) and for $x_0 \varepsilon$ (a,b), $f'(x_0) = 0$.

(Note that this means that x_0 is a critical point of f.)

(i) If $f''(x_0) < 0$, then f has a **local maximum** at x_0.

(ii) If $f''(x_0) > 0$, then f has a **local minimum** at x_0.

(iii) If $f''(x_0) = 0$, then there is insufficient information

so you must use the FIRST DERIVATIVE TEST.